JAN

H~~~E

AND

ABROAD

TALES IN OLD DEVON DIALECT

BROAD STREET PUBLISHING

INDEX.

!SBN 978-0-9557019-6-2

Printed and bound in Great Britain by
Short Run Press Limited, Exeter

BROAD STREET PUBLISHING
Arden Cottage, Coombeshead Road, Highweek
Newton Abbot TQ12 !PZ
Tel +44 (0) 1626 365478

This facsimile edition of Jan Stewer's At Home and Abroad is published with
the kind permission of A J Coles's grandaughter, Mrs Barbara Harrington.

The publisher wishes to dedicate this book, with affection and thanks, to
Ida Heywood

EDITOR'S NOTE.

THE stories and anecdotes included in this
volume have been selected from the dialect
contributions of Jan Stewer to the pages of
"The Illustrated Western Weekly News" during
the Great War. Most of them were written
while the Author was on Active Service, those in
the section "Jan Stewer Abroad" having been
sent from Egypt. Consequently some of the
events occurred in circumstances peculiar to the
war period, as, for instance, the café incident in
"Lias Buzzacott's Two Ounces," which happened
during the rigid Government rationing of flour,
when no more than two ounces might be served
to one person for tea ; and the completing of the
"Nationality" form in "Jan Finds a Hotel."
For the same reason the lines "Stick it, Cheel"
have lost their original significance but have
been included "lest we forget," and as a small
tribute to the woman who stayed at home.

A. J. C.

Jan learns about Egypt.

WHEN they tole me 'twas ordained for me to go to Egyp' I cude'n 'ardly bleeve it. I did'n knaw nort about Egyp'. I knawed there was sitch a place, o' cou'se, but where 'twas to, or what 'twas like I cude'n say, no more'n a dunkey. I axed ev'rybody I cude think o', to zee if they cude give me any information about it, but none o'm wad'n much wiser than mezell. All as they cude tell me was that 'twas a doost of a long ways away, an' I knawed that much a'ready. One body said 'twas where the cokynits come from and the monkeys comes and bites 'ee while you'm asleep. Another wan tole me twas the tother zide of India, 'long about Chinay an' Jericho an' all they places where the black folks lives to. An' some said there was lyons an' taygers by the thousan's, an' elephants rinnin' about like rabbuts, an' allygaters as long as a church.

'Ow-hever, wan day I got in comp'ny with a passon chap into the Y.M.C.A. place, an' I reckoned he'd be a very gude feller to knaw all about it, bein' eddicated in a manner o' spaikin'. So I brought up the subjec'.

" Gwain to Egyp', be 'ee ? " he saith. " That's a very interestin' place to go to. Most interestin' place in the wordle, I reckon. Daun' you remember, that's where Moses led the Israelites out o' captivity ? "

"Aw, is it, zur?" I says. "Praps I might come across 'en out there."

Caw, did'n he laaf.

"Why, 'twas thousan's o' years agone," he saith.

"Aw, was it?" I saith. "Then he'm daid by now for certin, poor feller."

"Daun' you remember about Vairo's darter?" he says to me.

Wull, o' cou'se, he ketched me all on the 'op as the sayin' is an' I wad'n thinkin' about they old ancient times. I did'n vathom what he was on upon fer a bit.

"I can't caal 'en home fer the minute, zur," I saith. "Was he wan of Muddle-come? You daun' mean Aaron Row's darter, ovver to 'Orcome?"

"Naw, naw! Vairo's darter was a princess in Egyp'."

"Aw, wull," I says. "That wad'n Poll Row, fer certin. Her was a laundress to Barleycome."

"Vairo's darter," he said, "found Moses in the bullrishes."

"What, was he pixy-led?" I says.

"Pixy-led? What do that mean?"

He wad'n Deb'mshur, fer certin.

"Wull," I says. "Was he a li'l bit thereafter, as the sayin' is? How did he come to lost hissell in they bullrishes?"

"He was aunly a li'l tiddy baby," he saith. "Somebody putt 'en there, an' Vairo's darter vound 'en."

"Aw, ees, o' cou'se," I says. "Now you come to mention it I du mind zummat about it. I've yerd passen tell about it. But I didn' connect it with Egyp' fer the minute."

2

" Same place," he saith.

" Aw, wull," I says, " I mus' take gude care I daun' go forragin' around in no bullrishes. I shude look well if I was to vind a cheel or two sticked about, shude'n I ? "

Caw ! Did'n he laaf ! I thort he never wad'n gwain to stap.

However, I ab'm come aross no-jis thing, thanks be.

The same passen-chap tole me ever so many interestin' things there was to be zeed in Egyp'. He said I was to be sure to look out for the spinks or some sitch thing.

I did'n quite ketch his meanin' at first, and so I says, " Yas," I says, " I've yerd that they furrin' contries do smell a bit high at times."

When he'd done laafin' he tole me the spinks was a big statute sticked up in the middle o' the desert. I think he said 'twas ha'f a wumman an' ha'f a lyon. Or whe'er 'twas the other way around I dunnaw. Be-as-twill, I ab'm zeed no sign o' sitch thing so fur. If ever I do ketch sight o't I'll let 'ee knaw. But, 'pon me zaul, wan yers sitch tales nawadays that you dunnaw what to believe 'ardly. P'raps there never was sitch a person, although I've yerd of a baby that had a pig's face.

O' cou'se, when I come to think o't there was heaps o' things I larned about Egyp' when I use to go to Zindy-skule. Arter I got into the contry I said wance to a chap what had been there ever so long :

" Why," I said, " this is the contry where they 'ad the ten plagues, id'n it ? "

3

" Yas," he said. " But that was a long time ago. They've invented a lot o' new wans since then."

An' wan other occasion I mind when us was out on the ole dessert I said to a chap,

" I was jis tryin' to remimber," I said, " what 'twas they Isralite folk use to get to ait when they was out in the dessert. I knaw 'twas orwiz the same thing, day arter day, cuz they complained about it, if I remimber rightly."

" I knaw what that must a-bin," he says. " Must a-bin machonochie stew."

Lines written during the " dark days " early in 1918, to a soldier's wife.

STICK IT, CHEEL !

When your soul is sick with waiting,
   Stick it, cheel ;
When the whole world reeks with hating,
   Stick it, cheel ;
When it seems we'm doin' bad,
An' you can't stop bein' sad,
Till you veels like gwain mad,
   Stick it, cheel.

Though the war drags on and on,
   Stick it, cheel ;
Though the power to hope seems gone,
   Stick it, cheel ;
Though you'm wore to rames with pining,
Can't discern no silver lining,
Cus the sun's gived over shining,
   Stick it, cheel.

4

Though you'm done right out to-end,
        Stick it, cheel ;
Though they've killed another friend,
        Stick it, cheel ;
Though you has to laugh and lie
When the tucked-in kiddies cry
Cuz their daddy's never nigh,
        Stick it, cheel.

Though you dream about that " wire,"
        Stick it, cheel ;
Till your brain is all afire,
        Stick it, cheel ;
Though you've got it in your head,
Until everything goes red,
That you'm gwain to hear he's dead,
        Stick it, cheel.

Though your faith melts into doubt,
        Stick it, cheel ;
Though the lights in heaven goes out,
        Stick it, cheel ;
They be only ovvercast—
Soon the mists will all be passed,
Us'll come out top at last,
        So stick it—stick it, cheel.

On the Big Ship.

I SHALL never virget when they fus'
putt me on the big ship to zen' me
out to furrin parts.   Dear soce !
What a scummer that was to be sure.

When I zeed all they hunderds o' sawjers
herded together in the harbour place, there
to Zouthampton, I thort to mezell, " where
fer heaven's sake be 'um gwain to putt 'um
all to ?   Never have ships enough to carr'
all this lot, fer certin."

If anybody had told me they was all
gwain to be putt 'pon wan ship, I'd 'ave
caaled en—Wull, there, I dunnaw what I
shude 'ave caaled en.   'Twude depend on
the size o'n.

An' then they took us up long-zide the
ship.

My hivers !   I was proper frightened to
zee 'en.   'Twas like lookin' up to a rove of
houses.   'Ow-hever sitch thing rides 'pon-
tap the watter bates me completely.

Darn 'ee cheel, her was as long as
Muddlecome Fore strate, from the pump
right up home to the church geat.

An' what comes ovver me, he'm all made
of ire.   I never knawed before that ire
wude ride pon-tap the watter.   I cude
understand if 'twas a timbern ship, cuz any
fule knawth that timber waunt sinky.

But ire floatin' about pon-tap the watter,
that's redecklus.

Wull there, winders 'ull never cease.

'Twas a funny feelin', gwain into thik ole ship. Us had to go scraalin' up a bit of a drangways, duck fashin. 'Twas turrable steepy, an' a doost of a long ways up to the tap, an' when you'm humpin' a gurt heavy ole bag 'pon yer shoulder an' two-dree things to the tother hand and a rifle bezides, 'tis a bit ockerd to scammle up a thing fer all the gude in the world like walkin' up a elevater.

If it had'n bin fer the chap be'ind shovin' me along, I daun' bleeve I ever shude a-got to the tap.

Not that he was doin' it out o' kindness, mind you. I wude'n think that fer wan instant. 'Twas a case of eetherways he shovin' me up or me shovin' he down. An' as there was a score more chaps comin' on be'ind, he winned ev'ry time.

What frightened me most when I got up on the floor o' the ship (or darned if I knaws whe'er 'twas the floor or the roof, but they calls it the deck), what frightened me was where they was puttin' all they chaps to. Scores an' hunderds there was, comin' along, cuz they were straimin' up thik ole drangways fer hours without ceasin'. When they'd get about a hunderd or so together 'pon tap the deck, all of a sudden they'd all disappear down a hole.

Then a hunderd or two more wude be pooked up together, and down they'd go down the hole, an' then a few more hunderds behind they.

You tell about gettin' the weend up as the sayin' is. I'm popped if I did'n.

O' cou'se I thought they must be all gwain down into the say. I cude'n zee for the

7

life o' me where else they cude be gwain to.

"Gude laur!" I thinks to mezell.
"Will it be my turn bim-bye?"

An' sure 'nuff, 'twas.

"Fall in," the sargent olleyed to we.

"Darn if I be gwain to fall in," I says
to mezell. "If I've got to go in somebody
will have to push me in."

However, when come all to all us did'n
go down in the say, 't all. There was steps
down this-yer hole, jis like gwain down the
ole underground railway. An' when you
got down the bottom there was room fer
hunderds of 'ee to walk about. An' then
there was more steps. An' down below
there was room fer hunderds more folks.
You cude strake about zactly same as if
you was in a church, aunly you had to be
careful you did'n knack yer haid.

There was heaps o' things about, jis the
right heighth to ketch 'ee. I think I must
a-vound most o'm.

An' then I be dalled if there wad'n more
steps to go down.

"My dear zaul!" I says. "I shan't
never vind me way up out o' this fer certin.
I be gwain clane down in the bowels o' the
earth, or the bowels o' the watter, I shude
say." An' then when us got down fur 'nuff
to plaise 'em, an' a sight too fur to plaise
me, us was told to hang up our kit an' get
back pon-tap the deck again.

Tell about hangin' up yer kit! All very
well fer they what was dapper, an' choosed
a place quick. But I wad'n way-wise, an'
by the time I'd blinked me eyes a couple o'
times an' lookid around there wad'n a place
left to hang up me 'at, never mind about

8

me kit, an' I had the whole lot knackin' about from piller to paust all the way across. Vifty times a day I use to go around an' gather up odds an' ainds from where they'd bin kicked to last. Purt' near drove me mazed that did.

An' arter all, when us got ovver tother zide, I was wan boot missin' an' me watter-bottle, an' had to pay fer the baggers.

But I got in the way o' bein' more dapper arter a bit. That's wan thing sawjerin' larns 'ee. It larns 'ee to look arter number wan.

Davey Jones's Locker and the Mermaids.

I RECKON you dunnaw old David Jones, do 'ee? He lives down bottom o' the say. From what I can gather he've a-got a locket, and ev'rything that goes down in-under the say go'th into David Jones's locket.

I sim he must be a middlin'-size locket. My missis have a-got wan o' the soort, which belonged to her gurt gran'mother, or thereabouts, an' he's ha'f so-big as a turmit. But he wude'n hold ha'f-quatter the things that have gone down bottom o' the say, aunly to my knowledge.

'Twas wan o' the sailor chaps on the gurt ship told me all about it. Very affable chap he was, an' he'd zeed some marvellous things, upon my word.

· He reckoned he'd zeed old David Jones scores o' times. Zummat to do with a Quaker, he said he was, but I did'n exac'ly ketch that part properly. Whe'er he said David was a Quaker hissell, or whe'er he'd zeed 'en along of a Quaker, I can't jis tell 'ee fer sure. An' I did'n care to ax 'en to keep repaitin' hissell, 'feared he wude'n like it.

However, he was abble to tell me that David had a-got long green wiskers an' a turrable rid nawse, so he must a-zeed 'en fer certin. Though how he got his rid nawse, bein' in the say all the time, I can't imagine.

But the most winderfle thing of all, David have got a passell o' maidens about the place, which he keeps same purpose to 'coy the ships into dangerous places, so's they shall be wrecked, an' go down bottom o' the say. Then all the things that is inside goes into his locket.

Not ordnery maidens they ban't. They'm w'at they caals mermaidens, an' very coorious lookin' they must be, by all accounts. Up-about, they'm zacly like butifle maidens, with 'mazing long hair an' hansum vaces. But down-about, they'm finished off with a tail like a rid-errin'. They'm terrors to swim, an' they makes nothin' to keep up along with any ship, never mind how vast her can go.

But they'm a proper bad lot, thase yer mermaidens, fer-all they'm so ansum-looking. You can't trist 'em a minute, for they'll lead 'ee astray. 'Tis all they'm after, the brazen vaggots, that ever I shude say sitch thing.

They've got mos' lovely voices fer singin', sim-so. Of a night sometimes you can yer 'em zingin' the most butifle zongs, like as if they was angels floatin' tap the watter. I never yerd wan mezell, that I knaws by, but this-yer sailor chap he'd yerd 'em auf'n of a night in wan ship he used to ride in. But lucky fer he the cap'm chap what use to guide the ship was a grainy ole toad what 'ad bin married vower times, an' each wive was wiss-tempered an' more crabbid than the wan avore. So he'd gived up all truck with the women-volk, an' no mermaidens ner nort else cude'n temp' he.

But sometimes the cap'm is a youngish chap, with a heye fer a purty maiden, an' he'd volley arter 'em with his ship, an' not consider where he was gwain to, an' they'd swim along bevore 'en, an' zing up their butifle moosic, an' 'tice 'en on to a place where there's nasty gurt rocks in under the watter. An' all of a sudden the ship wude rin scat up agin they ole rocks an' be tore all abroad, an' down wude go the whole contraption, sailors an' all to the bottom o' the say. And David Jones wude putt 'em all into his locket.

An' then the maidens wude stap singin' drec'ly, an' begin to laaf. But tis sitch a ojis laaf that the vishes jumps right up out o' the watter into the air. An' that's how there comes to be flyin' vish.

I mus' say I shude a-liked to a-zeed jis wan o' they mermaidens, an' I kainid about a gudish bit, but I never ketch sight o' noan

I did yer a quare sort of a noise in the middle o' the night, wance, an' I thought to mezell, " P'raps that's a mermaiden." So I waked up the chap next to me to zee whe'er he thought 'twas or no. But he were a turrable seb'm sleeper, an' by the time I got 'en to his sainses the noise had stapped.

" What's matter ? " he says, rubbin' the place where I waked 'en up to.

" 'Tis orright," I says. " I thought I yerd a mermaiden zingin', an' I wanted for you to tell me whe'er 'twas or no."

" Yerd a what ? " he saith, sittin' up.

" A mermaiden," I says. " One o' they maidens what lives in the watter an' 'tices the poor sailors to the rocks."

My dear zaul, the coose things thik feller did say to be sure. If he did'n call me but ev'rything. Properly annoyed he was.

" You better-way let the doctor zee you avore you gets any wiss," he saith, " or else take more watter with it."

Jan goes up in the Air.

YES, they said to me, "Jan, wude you like to go up in airyoplane?" Aw-haw! My dear days! Wude I like to go up in airyoplane?

How many times had I stood there with me heart comin' up in me mouthe to zee the capers they chaps did preform up in the air? There was a time when folks wude go miles to zee a flyin' chap loop the loop. Now, begad, he'll turn his ole machine tap-an-tail to get his matches out from his pocket.

Ev'ry day I use to zee 'em up to their ole items when I was to Suez, by the ole Suez Canal, cuz the Flyin' Corpse camp was aunly nex-door to ours as you mid zay.

An' what outrageous manoovers they wude·get up to!

They'd ride their ole machines vorrads, back'ards, zideways, up'n-down or in'n-out. They'd make 'em spin like a top or rin around like the 'obby-'osses. They'd make 'em 'op, skip an' jump, rear up, lie down, roll ovver, tie theirzells in knots, rin arter their tails, sit up an' beg, stand on their haid, waltz, poker, shotteeze, turn zummer-zets—any mortle thing but talk. They'd go right up into the sky till they wad'n no more'n a speck, an' then let theirzells vall down like a dead burd, fus' wan zide an' then tother, till you must shut yer eyes not to zee the poor veller scat all abroad to flibbits. An' then, jis when you'd think he had'n but wan more minute to live, the ole airyoplane wude stap an' pull hissell together, look around, an' way-da-go like a hawk.

An' then they said to me, " Jan, wude'n 'ee like to go fer a ride in a airyoplane ? "

" Yas," I said. " When the pigs vlies then you mid zee ole Jan Stewer vlyin'. Not bevore."

" I was given two veet," I says, " same purpose to walk 'pon tap the floor. If it had bin ordained fer me to go up there along o' the zun by day an' the mune an' the stars by night I shude a-bin supplied with wings like the ducks. Ducks can't vly nothin' to boast about, but if me an' a duck was to start together from a airyoplane I shude vancy his chance a lot better'n mine. I derzay I shude ween the race, so fur as that's consarned, but I seem he'd vinish in the better condition."

But it jis shaws 'ee what poor vules us men-volk be. Wan mornin' I was stood gappin' to the airyoplanes gwain up, an' there was wan stood there all in raddiness, an' bim-bye the chap come out what was gwain to ride in 'en, an' when he zeed me he saith, " Ullaw, Jan, be 'ee comin' up fer a ride ? 'Tis a butifle day fer't."

An' what possessed me I dunnaw, ner I can't think. But I lookid to he, an' I lookid to the ole airyoplane. An' he was a fine upstandin' veller as ever stood in butes, with his leathern jacket an' cap an' his funny sparticles up ovver the tap of his haid. An' he 'ad a merry-lookin' vaace like a sunny mornin', an' a twinkle in his eye that shude a-made me more cautious.

" Thank 'ee, zur. If you mind to have me I shall be plaised to come."

The words was out o' me mouthe bevore I 'ardly knawed w'at I was tellin' about.

" Come on, then," he saith. An' off us goes, me winderin' what I'd done, an' whe'er 'twas too late or no to alter it.

I volleyed 'en ovver across where the ole contraption was stood to. Tremenjis high he did zim when I got bezide 'en, an' a lot bigger than I thort. Like a hugly gurt grasshopper he looked, with wheels fer legs, an' his gurt wings spread out all raddy to fly away soon's ever I got inzide.

" Go on, Jan, clim up," says the chap.

" Pilot," they caaled 'en. Whe'er 'tis short for Ponshus Pilot or no I dunnaw, but I shude think it ort to be.

" I dunnaw so much about climmin up, zur," I zaith. " I ban't so flippant as I use to be."

However, with wan pullin' above an' a couple pushin' below they managed to get me up ovver the side into the back sate.

'Tis a funny ole place when you'm inzide. You'm sot down so low, aunly yer haid comes ovver the side. I was glad o' that, cuz there wad'n so much likelihudes o' vallin' out ovver. An' there id'n no rume to go scammelin' yer veet about, nuther. There's all manner of hannles an' gadjits which you muzzen titch 'pon no account.

Pilot cautioned me most pa'ticler about they. " They hannles will move about when us be vlyin'," he saith, " an 'if you gets in the way o'm us'll very likely come down quicker than us intainded.."

Laur massey! I never watched nothin' so keen in all me life as I did they hannles. If they'd bin kings an' quanes I cude'n a-paid more rispect to 'em.

Nex' thing they do'd was to putt a sort o' cap on me haid an' tie 'en in under me cheen wi' two bits o' coord. There was two stiff inji-rubber pipes belongin' to thisyer cap, an' they was 'tached to the side o' the airyoplane. I reckoned they was to keep me from lainin' me haid too fur out ovver the zide. 'Twas a very gude idaya, I derzay, but they needn' a-bin anxious. There wad'n much fear o' me lainin' out ovver. Soon's I sot down I was about as lissom as a gun-bareel.

Then Mester Pilot he climmed into the airyoplane an' zot down in front o' me, like he meant business. And then all the things come into me mind that I'd ever yerd about dredful accidents which had hap'med to volks in airyoplanes, an' I was glad I'd changed me socks an' putt on clean underclothes an' had a gude bath, cuz I knawed that was the fust thing my missis wude ax me. Orwiz, if I didn't change me shirt 'ardly so quick as her thort I ought to her used to say, " Whatever wude you veel like if you was killed all of a sudden an' they was to find 'ee wearin' a dirty shirt ? "

Pilot he exercised all his hannles to zee if they was orright, an' I was prayin' hard behind that there'd be zummat wrong wi' wan o'm, so's us cude'n go. When he moved his hannles the wans bezide me all moved at the zame time, an' I thort to

17

mezell, " That's orright, Jan. If you can aunly vind out the wan which makes the bagger stap, you can stap 'en yerzell when you've 'ad sufficient."

But then I thort to mezell, " What's the gude o' stappin' o'n if us be 'bout a hunderd miles up in the air ? "

So that wad'n no gude.

Then a feller climmed up into the ole airyoplane an' made fast a gurt leathern strap around me waist. 'Tis a quare zort of a zinsation to think you'm in a place where they've got to putt a kickin' strap on 'ee to keep 'ee from vaalin' out. I thought to mezell, " Spausin' the ole girth shude break. Where shude I be to, then ? " An' I ketched hold to thik strap, my dear, wi' both hands, so's if he shude hap'm to break by any chance I shude be hangin' on by the two ainds.

An' I never let 'en go genst us was back 'pon the vloor agean. I'll make a bet the marks o' my nails be in 'en to this day.

Then another chap started twistin' around the ole wirligig thing in front, what they caals a compeller. An' all of a zudden away he started wizzin' around wi' sitch a roar an' a racket I shude a-jumped clane out o' me sate if it had'n a-bin fer the ole kickin' strap.

Then I knawed I was in fer't, purty quick.

Pilot waggled his hannles a time or two an' then made meanings to the chaps that was holdin' back the machine to let 'en go. I was jis' 'pon the point of holleyin' to 'em to ketch 'en hold again ; but I was too-laate.

Us was on the move a-raddy, an' bevore

you cude zay Jack Robinson the ole airyo-plane was coosin' along the ground like a gurt rooster with his wings spread out an' the vox arter 'en. Vaster an' vaster us waint but nort hap'm'd.

Then I thort the ole machine sim to be gettin' winderfle tall. An' he got taller an' taller like as if the wheels was grawin' bigger. So I glimpsed out ovver the zide to zee if 'twas so.

Aw, my dear zaul. Us was up in the air !

I took wan look to zee if there was a chance to get back. But 'twas too-laate.

Us was high as a houze.

Us was high as a church.

Us was high as the canthedral into Exeter.

An' us was gwain higher.

'Tis a turrable weesh sinsation, my dear, when you zees the earth an' all that therein is drappin' down an' down away from 'ee, an' nothin' to connect 'ee together.

There was no way out o't now. Let come what may I must bide where I was to, an' aunly be too thankful if I was allowed to do that.

Arter a bit me mind begin to settle down like a potvul o' boilin' dumplins took off the vire. An' I must say 'twad'n bad trav'lin'. Her glides along more suant than any other vayicle ever I rawd in. Aunly, o' cou'se you've got a vunny veelin' all the time that if her shude take it into her haid to stap still an' go straight 'ome, 'twill be a anxious time comin' to the bump.

But when you do get sufficient courage to look out ovver the zide 'tis like a noo

19

world, very winderfle to behold. I a'most fergot to be feared, I was so tooked up wi' the wonderfulness o't. An' then I beginned to try to pick out the places I knawed. In the town I cude zee the strates, not like I'd bin used to zee 'em, wan to a time (an' not very much o' that), but all to wance, straked out like a gurd-iron. An' where the churches shude be, or moskies as they caals 'em out there, I cude jis trace a li'l white square like a lump o' shugger.

I cude zee the gas-works like a couple o' small pill boxes, an' the camp looked like a lot o' zixpences lied on the ground.

That was all well an' gude, so-long as the ole airyoplane went on suant an' rispectable. 'Twas when her started her ole migrations that the trouble beginned.

The fust inklin' I had that anythin' was wrong was arter us had vlied ovver the harbour place where the ships was to.

You knaws, o' cou'se, what the wings of a airyoplane is like. Wull, when you'm close to 'em they'm a tremenjis size, an' when you'm sot in the machine up in the air tiz a sort of a comfert to 'ee to zee they gurt fellers sticked out each side of 'ee. You'm plaized to zee zummat so big an' broad an' level like, an' you knaws that so-long as they bides there you'm orright.

Wull, as I zay. I was lookin' out ovver the zide, an' jis beginnin' to get reconciled as the sayin' is, when all to wance I zeed zummat draidful hap'm. Fust I cude'n believe me eyes. I thought they was desayvin' me. But no. 'Twas true ; an' me heart come right up into me mouthe, an' I went all ovver preckles. The 'air on

20

me 'aid stood up like a vuz bush, an' if me cap 'ad'n bin tied on wi' coord he'd a-bin pushed clane off.

The ole wing, the aunly bit o' comfort I'd got all up there in the bright blue sky was dippin' down'ards at the far aind! Gwain down an' down he was, graj'ly towards the ground. An' when I looked out the tother zide, the oppozite wing was gwain up!

The darned ole airyoplane was tippin' ovver wan zide! An' the ground more'n a mile away!

The little brains there was inzide me haid started rishin' around an' kep' valin' over theirzells. I was 'ot as vire an' cold as aice. I holleyed to Pilot to take care, but the ole wirlygig was creatin' sitch a clatter he cude'n yer me. An' still us was lainin' ovver more an' more 'till I was lookin' to the ground out o' the corner o' me eye. An' all the time tryin' to push the ole consarn into a upright position.

An' then zummat else hap'm'd which jist about drove the las' bit o' conscience out o' me body. I yerd a loud voice behind me olley out, "Let yerzel go wi' the machine."

Behine me, mind!

Lor' soce, if 't ad'n a-bin for the kickin' strap I shude a-bin clane out o' the airyoplane. I turned me haid around to zee who 'twas talkin' to me an' there wad'n nobody there.

Aw dear, aw dear! thinks I to mezell, us have got up that high us be in amongs' the ghosts o' the daid folk. An' I thought

21

to mezell, " 'Twaun' be so very long afore I'm wan mezell."

An' with the same, I yerd the voice again, " Let yerzel go with the machine."

An' then I zeed the way o't. You mind I told 'ee they fastened a cap on me haid wi' a couple o' pipes attached to 'en. I thought they was to keep me from lainin' out ovver too fur. But they wad'n nothin' o' the soort. They was spaikin' chubes. An' Maister Pilot he was olleyin' down tother aind.

But aw, my dear, aunly to think o't. There was me right up in the sky higher than the burds, wi' nothin', as you mid say, between me an' kingdom-come in either direction, with the ole contrivance turnin' ovver p'n wan side, an' then zomebody tells 'ee, " Let yerzell go wi' the machine."

Darn 'ee, I wanted to knaw where the machine was gwain to fust.

But laur' bless 'ee, cheel, that was aunly the start o' me troubles. When the ole machine had lied ovver so-fur as her cude goo wan way her tooked it into her haid to lain ovver tother way. 'Twude'n a-bin so bad if I'd knawed what her intentions was. But all I knawed was that us was gwain droo all kinds of manoovers up in the air, an' I cude'n zay whe'er us was doin' 'em on purpose or by accident.

An' the wist o't was, the heavens above an' the earth beneath begin to behave theirzells in the most onraisonable manner. The town, an' the harbour, an' the deep blue zay, an' the hills went shootin' about all ovver the place. Wan minute the houses wude be to the right o' me an' the

22

hills to the left o' me, an' the sky above in the proper place, where it was intended to be accordin' to the Tain Commandments. An' then all to a sudden the whole world wude shift. The town wude go rushin' away towards the mountins ; the mountins flipped up into the sky ; the harbour an' ships went coo'sin from east to west ; the heavens came down on airth, an' the airth went up to heaven. Tell about the hills skippin' like young rams. They jumped like ole kangaroons.

I derzay you'll think, " Poor ole Jan Stewer have gone mazed. The hot zin in Egyp' have affected his brain.."

But I can assure 'ee soce, that's azac'ly what it all simmed like to me. An' then quick as lightnin' they wude all flip back again where they was bevore. But aunly fer a minute. All to wance the fore part o' the machine wude point down'ards an' off us wude go wi' a mighty rish towards the airth. I soon larned to knaw that this meaned more trouble. Soon's us 'ad got up a turrable speed, they'd all dap off again ; the mountins dancin' to the zay, an' the zay standin' up on aind, the houses hangin' up in the sky, an' the sky down 'pon the floor.

O' cou'se, I knaws very well it was we that was twestin' about, an' not the firma-mint. But I'm tellin' 'ee what it appears like when you'm ridin' in airyoplane.

And to-last me poor ole haid got that dizzy with seein' the houses jumpin' ovver the mountins, an' the ships sailin' around in the sky, that I was fo'ced to shut me eyes ev'ry time us started off on some fresh migrations.

An' arter a bit Pilot turned around, an' I imagine he was a bit surprised to vind me still there. But I was hangin' on to the ole kickin' strap orright, you can't make no mistake.

An' when he vound he cude'n emp' me out he thort he'd goo 'ome. So us come down, an' they lifted me out an' putt me on the ground.

An' if ever you hears that Jan Stewer have gone flyin' again you'll knaw 'tis because he've turned into a angel.

A Visit to the Pyramids and Sphinx.

S O now I'll tell 'ee all about how me an'
Micky Doyle went to zee they ole
Primitives and the Spinks while us
was to Cairo.

Wull, there, I keeps on caalin' it
Primitives. Tid'n Primitives at all, 'tis
Pirrimids. Micky tooked a lot o' trouble
to taiche me to say it proper, but I got
Primitives in me haid fust, an' when wance
I gets a thing into me haid I've got a middlin'
job to shift'n.

An' tid'n Spinks, nuther, although it
looks zummat like it in print. He's a
nuisance of a word to pronounciate. You've
got to say " Sfinks." But Micky advised
me to give up tryin' he, cuz the volks used
to think I was op'min a bottle o' soda-
watter, an' the rush fer drinks was liable
to cause a panic.

However, I 'ad a gude try to master 'en,
an' Micky says, " Turn the tother way, Jan.
I ab'm got me anbrella, an' if I gets wet
through I shall ketch cold fer certin."

O' cou'se, 'tis through the means o' me
losing me eye teeth. If twad'n fer that I
cude say " Sfinks " orright wai'out spranking
anybody.

Us rawd out all the way in a tram. Us
got in the tram there to Cairo City an' us
never got out genst us was up home to the

Spinks—Sfinks. Tremenyus long ole ride. I shude'n never a-thort there cude be a tram line the length. Lectrisical trams, o' cou'se. They'm proper up-to-date out there to Egyp'.

You goes right ovver across the River Nile, ovver the Castor Oil Bridge, or some sitch name, an' then straight rawd fer miles right out to the dessert. You can zee the track fer miles ahaid of 'ee, an' there's a proper vine carriage rawd rins alongside with butifle trees both zides.

'Tis very intrestin' gwain along. All zorts o' black volks comes an' zits bezide 'ee, an' eats monkey-nits. Terrors they be fer eatin' monkey-nits. They'm eetherways eatin' monkey-nits, smockin' zigarettes, or chowin' sugar-cane.

All of a zudden Micky says, " There's the Pirrimids, Jan, look'ee."

" Where to ? " I says.

" There, right ahaid of 'ee."

" Gude laur," I says. " Why, they'm jis like they be on the picter pos'cards."

" Wull, did 'ee expect 'em to be differnt then ? " says Micky.

" You knaw what I mean," I says. " I seem they look turrible smaal."

" You'm a long ways off, remember," says Micky. " If you was stood on top o' wan o' they pirrimids you wude'n be abble to zee yerzelf at all not from this distance."

They ban't very much to look to when you fust glimpses 'em. Aunly two or dree humps gwain up to a point, and a dark-lookin' colour. I mus' say when I fust zeed 'em, I thought 'twas stoobidness fer folks to come all ovver the world to see they things.

Bim-bye us come to the end o' the tram-line, an' then us got on a couple o' dunkeys. There's orwis hosts o' chaps there with dunkeys an' camels waitin' fer towerists, an' they'll chait 'ee right an' left if you daun' watch 'em. If you do watch 'em they'll chait 'ee vore an' back. They'll chait 'ee anyway.

Wull, us went up around the rawd an' come up agin what they terms the Gurt Pirrimid. That's the bigges' o' the lot, an' there's dree o'm altogether, but the tother two is a trifle smaller.

But laur' bless 'ee, 'tis when you gets up handy to the ole veller that you zees what a treemenyus size he be. 'Tis all created from 'normous gurt stones. Each stone is purt' near so big over as the kitchen table an' about the same heighth. The bottom o' the ole Pirrimid mus' cover up vower or vive acres o' land I shude think, with vower square zides, an' he goes up in roves an' roves o' thase yer monstrous gurt stones. An' ev'ry rove is one stone less all the way around, so when you looks up the zide 'tis like gurt stonen staps gwain right up to a point. Some folks clims up thase yer staps to the tap, but not fer Jo ! Micky wanted fer me to go up. But I says, " No, thank 'ee, Micky, if 'tis all zame to you I'll bide where I be to. I'll take your word fer't that the tap stone is the highest wai'out gwain up to prove it."

They tell'th me that they Pirrimids have been there fer thousands o' years. Nobody knaw'th fer certin how old they be azac'ly. 'Tis suppaused that ole Fairo or wan o' they ole ancient Kings of Egyp' putt'n up fer a kind of a tombstone ovver his missis.

"Putt a-plenty o' weight 'pon her chest," says Micky. "He had'n no intentions of her ever comin' up again, that's fer certin."

But it do seem coorious that anybody shude want to erec' sitch enormous gurt constructions right out there in the dessert. How they got the stones there I can't think, cuz o' cou'se the trams is all new since then. An' how they erected 'em arter they had 'em there beats me intirely.

An' w'at's the gude o't all arter tiz done ? Nobody can't live in 'em. You can looky to 'em ; an' arter you've said that you've said ev'rything.

Then us went another ha'f a mile or zo down ovver a steep dip in the sand, an' zeed the ole Spinks—Sfinks.

Her's a quare lookin' ole toad her is, sure 'nuff. I dunnaw how to discribe her to 'ee hardly.

Her's as big as a gurt houze, an' her's zummat the shape of a vower-liggid animal lied down, with a wumman's faitures. Some volks say that wance upon a time her was very butifle to look to, but it must a-bin a doost of a long time agone.

They say her have a-bin there thousands o' years, too, an' I be darned if her daun' look it.

Nowadays her 'ave aunly got a gurt 'ole where her nawse ort to be, an' her eyes is the wiss fer wear. If her's a sample o' w'at the women use to be in they ole ancient days I daunt winder they use to keep their faces covered ovver 'till arter they was married.

They tells 'ee a bit of a ditty about the ole Sfinks that wance upon a time when her was alive her use to ax a riddle of ev'rybody that come along.

" Fust I goes 'pon vower ligs, then 'pon two, then 'pon dree."

That was the riddle, an' if you cude fathom it you cude marry her, but if you did'n then her'd ait 'ee up. So fur as I'm consarned I dunnaw whe'er I'd zooner 'ave married her or bin ait up.

However, nobody cude'n fathom it, an' all they what tried was ait up. Then, to-last another chap come along an' had a go at it. Micky saith he was a Irishman, but whe'er that's true or no I can't zay. But I'm purty sure he wad'n a Deb'mshur chap, else he wude'n have no truck wi' sitch tomfoolishness.

However, this-yer chap reckoned the answer to the riddle was a Man. When he'm a babby he go'th 'pon vower ligs, an' then he larns to walk 'pon two legs ; an' then bim-bye when he get'th old an' cripple he'm fo'ced to use a stick, an' that's dree ligs.

An' then I suppaus the ole Missis Sfinks was so tooked aback to think that anybody should fathom her ole riddle that her turned into stone like Lot's wive. Aunly Lot's wive turned into zalt, which is more useful.

Be-as-twull, I've zeed the Pirrimids an' the Spinks—Sfinks, an' very glad to 'ave the opportunity. But I'd zooner zee Haytor Rock or Belliver Tor any time.

29

Some Notions of Cairo.

THEY said to me, "Jan, what did 'ee think o' Cairo, thik gurt city in Egyp'?"

An' I said, "I dunnaw, cheel, what I did think."

Now that's a fulish thing fer a fella to say arter he've bin there an' zeed it, id'n it?

But there 'tis. 'Tis true. When I tries to raycall what I zeed to Cairo—meaning to say, o' cou'se, the native parts, like the Moushky, I can't get no details. Only notions. I can't piece out the differnt things wan to time, an' say I zeed this thing or that thing, or the tother. 'Tis all boxed up as you mid say into notions.

If you mind to have they notions, sitch as they be, you'm welcome.

Wull, the fust notion that is in my mind about they Cairo places is COLOUR. Rid, blue, yaller, green, ev'ry imaginable colour, like as if you'd took the big church winder to bits an' mix-muddle 'en all 'pon the floor. The crowds is all coloured, cuz the men dresses in rid hats, an' blue gowns, an' rid sashes round their waist, or blue hats an' rid gowns an' green sashes, or yaller, or brown, or any other colour you can think of. An' the donkeys has rid cloths ovver their backs, or green or blue, or all the lot.

An' carpets o' the most gorgeous colours hangs up outside the funny li'l shops, an' there's heaps o' green fruit, an' yellow fruit, an' rid fruit by the side o' the rawd, or on the barrers. An' there's the drink-sellers, they'm all to a glitter o' shinin' brass, and the sun making everything stare with brightness. An' all they colours has got mixed up in my brain an' made what you mid caal a notion. A notion of Cairo.

An' the next notion I've got is MOVEMENT. Now, o' cou'se, you'll say that's stoobid. cuz there's movement in ev'ry place. If you goes up to Lunnon you wude'n hardly say the volks was stood still all the while.

I knaws all about that, but 'tis differnt, if you understand my meanin'. If you'm to Lunnon you zees movement right nuff, but 'tis movement in straight lines, in a manner o' spaikin'. Ev'rybody is eether-ways gwain someplace or comin' back again. He knawth where he'm gwain to, an' he go'th there direc'. An' the volks this side the rawd. be gwain wan way, an' they on thikky zide be gwain tother.

But that id'n my notion o' Cairo. It simmed like as if the folks was shiftin' about jis' to keep the colours on the move an' make fresh patterns. It did'n zeem like they'd got any pa'ticler raison fer gwain wan way any more than tother. Jis' as though you had they bits of church winder an' kep' pushin' 'em about into different arrangements. In Lunnon the people strakes along an' makes like flowin' rivers. But in Cairo they moves, an' makes like tettivated ponds, everlastin' changin' shapes, and changin' colour. Anyhow, that's how it seems in my stoopid ole haid.

An' the nex' notion I've got is SMELL. O' cou'se, I bant tellin' about what you'd caal the up-to-date, or the European part o' the city. That's purty much the same as you mid vind in England. But the smells is part o' the native quarter, jis like the colour and the movement is part of it. An' they comes to 'ee jis the same way wai'out any rhyme or raison. Wan minute 'twill be summat that seems to bite at the back o' yer nawse, an' bevore you got time to think what it can be 'twill change to zummat zour an' 'orrid, an' you putts yer hand to veel fer yer hankcher. But bevore you can get 'en out there comes summat swit an' butifle like as if you'd stapped into a shop fulled wi' lovely flowers. An' you takes two sniffs at 'en to get more o't, an' the fust is all right, but the second is all garlic, or zummat which purt-near makes 'ee zick. An' you turns your haid a-wan zide to excape from it, an' gets a sniff o' baking corn, or shoein' horses, or a wumman passin' by will make 'ee zeem as if you'd took the cork out of a scent bottle an' putt it to your nawse. An' you'm never without a smell o' some soort. You jis' passes along from wan smell to tother, same as if you was gwain droo a gurt mansion you'd pass along from wan room to the next. The aunly smell you daun' get is the fresh air. You got to wait fer that, genst you come out tother end o' the strate.

An' the other notion o' Cairo I've got in me haid is NOISE. Now, you gets noise up in Lunnon, plenty o't. But the Lunnon noise is low ; a rum'lin, rollin', roarin' sort o' noise, like what us use to caal the bass in the church choir. But in Cairo 'tis the tribble. A high noise ; a mixture of chitterin' an' chatterin', cryin' an' zinginn' with the Psalms drowed in, an' the tinklin' o' the zimbals, an' ev'rybody talkin', an' nobody ever stappin', an' nobody ever listenin'. An' a chap on the pavement will sharpen a zaw, an' his neighbour will grind his axe, an' nex' to 'en, is a chap hammerin' a pattern on a brassen tray, an' another holdin' a handful o' scritchin' fowls, an' then wan playin' a bagpipes with aunly dree notes which goes ovver an' ovver again for ever and ever, amen. An' all the volks in the quare li'l shops cries out what they'm sellin' (an' they'd sooner cry than sell any time), an' jis' behind 'ee a dunkey lifts up his voice an' wails out a turrible tale of grief an' woe, an' the noises goes up an' mixes with ten thousan' other noises all so much alike you can't tell tother from which, an' you can't distinguish any pa'tic'ler noise, but there's jist a sort of maze o' the whole lot, 'till the air seemth to be twitterin' with it.

When Jan Played Football.

WHAT I be gwain to tell 'ee about now hapm'd the time I was sawjerin' out to Egyp'. When you've yerd the whole rigmarole you'll zay, " Poor ole Jan Stewer never had'n got very much sainse best o' times, but I reckon the hot zin out there to Egyp' must a drove 'en clean mazed, ever to do jis-thing."

There was a dizzen or zo more officers bezides mezell living together there to Port Said. An' us was hard putt-to zometimes to knaw what to be on upon to pass away the time when us wad'n to-work.

So wan day us received a bit of a note from the officers in another ridgement axin' if us wude play a vootball match. Wull, o' cou'se I nivver paid much 'tention to it, but most o'm was turrable tooked up with the idaya, an' they sent back a letter to say Ees, they'd be most plaized to. Wull, natterally there was tremenjus excitement bout this ole vootball match, an' the chaps was like a passel o' skule-chillern ovver it. You'm ap' to get that way when you bin fer months right away from ev'rybody. 'Tis winderfle what li'l stoobid things will occupy yer mind.

Be that as it may, when come the day o' the match, wan o' the vootballin' chaps was took bad an' wad'n abble to play. An,

I be darned if the feller they caals the captin did'n come up to me an' say: "Stewer," he says, "you'll ha' to play in place o' Smith."

"That's right," I says. "Can't you fancy you sees me kickin' a football?"

"Never mind about fancy," he saith; "'tis realality. There waun' be very much for yu to do. You waun' ha' to rin about. Us wants fer 'ee to be gold-keeper."

"Aw, that'll suit me zac'ly," I says. "You fetch along the gold. I'll keep it orright."

Wull, 'twad'n a bit o' gude fer me to zay I wude'n ha' nort to do wai't. They trigged me out with a shirt like Josep's coat o' many colours an' a li'l pair o' short briches that did'n come down to me knees. Purty vine lookin' figure I was, I can 'sure 'ee, with me knees knackin' together ev'ry stap, an' lookin' like wan o' they zebra things in the zoologmical gardens, walkin' on his hine legs.

I kept on sayin' to 'em, "'Tis no gude you draggin' me out yer like this, makin' vule o' me an' yerzels as well. I dunnaw nort about yer ole vootball, an' I daun' want to vind out, nuther."

But I mid jis so well knack me haid agin the waal. If I'd lied down an' rayfused to movee, they'd a-took me up an' carr'd me. So I mid-so-well go quiet.

"You mus' do yer bes', Jan," they said. "'Tis fer the honour o' the mess."

"Giddout wi' yer rummage," I says. "I looks a fat lot like honour to the mess, daun' I? Should be more honour to the ole pantomine, I reckon."

"Never mine how you looks," they said. "I'll make a bet you'll play a jolly gude game o' vootball, an' show some o' they youngsters the way around."

Cou'se they was only pullin' my lig, as the sayin' is. But that's all they'm fit for, most o'm.

However, the tother chaps arrived all right. I had bin in hopes summat wude hap'm to prevent 'em comin', but it did'n. So they come. An' a bright lookin' lot o' sparks they was, too. They was all Medical Corpse, an' Ingineers, an' Army Audience, an' they sort o' chaps. Wan of our vellers says to me, " 'Tis orright, Jan, there's sivverl docters amongs' 'em. So if you shude hap'm to break yer neck they'll be abble to stick 'en together agean."

"Thank 'ee sure," I says, "fer they vew kine words."

"Wull, I dunnaw about docters, but from what I cude judge when us was playin' I shude think there was a vew stame-ingines amongs' 'em.

O' cou'se, us did'n play 'pon a grassen vield, same's they do home, fer the simple raison there ban't sitch thing in the contry. Us 'ad to play 'pon the zand.

"Yer's your gold-poastis, Jan," the cap'm zays, when us got to the place.

Wull, o' cou'se they wad'n gold. They was ord'nery timbern poastis, two stood upright 'bout a lan-yard an' arf apart, an' wan across the tap a bit higher than I cude raich.

"Now, Jan," says the cap'm, "all you got to do is to stan' there an' stap the baal from gwain droo they poasts."

" Sounds orright," I saith.

Wull, the chaps sticked theirsells about all ovver the place, an' the tother zide do'd the same. Us 'ad blue an' yaller shirts, an' tother vellers rid an' black, so's us cude tell wan from tother. Then there was a umpire feller what blawed a wissle ev'ry wips-wile. What fer, I dunnaw. But I discovered that when he blawed his wissle us was all spaused to stap kickin', 'genst he blawed agean.

Wull, when us was all in raddiness umpire blawed up a bit of a chune, an' zomebody gi' a kick to the baal, an' in wan minute they was all rishin' about like a passel o' colts.

I was thankful they putt me gold-keeper cuz I ad'n got nort to do, seps look at the tothers dappin' about like two-ligged grasshoppers. An' the sun shinin' hot as vire.

" Wull, Jan," thinks I to mezell, " if this is all fer 'ee to do, I reckon you cude'n make a better gold-keeper if you was born to it."

Jis then I zeed wan o' the rid-an'-black vellers rinnin' along with the baal in front o'n, like a train. Never zeed a chap rin so vast in me life.

Sivverl of our chaps tried to ketch 'en, but he laived 'em behind aisy. Rinnin' right towards me he was, so I got a gude view o'n. I was turrable intrested to zee how much furder he cude rin like it. when all to wance he give the baal a kick like a mule, an' it went flyin' past, not six foot from where I was stood to.

Then all the rid-an'-black chaps 'olleyed

out " Gold," an' started rinnin' back again.
But two-dree of our chaps come around me
an' spoke proper cross.

" Why did'n 'ee stap 'en, Jan ? "

" Stap what ? " I says.

" Why, the baal."

" What fer ? "

" What fer, yer mump'aid ? Why, that's
what you'm there fer."

" Is it ? " I saith. " Wull, if he wanted
me to stap'n, why did'n he kick'n where I
cude raich'n ? "

" You gurt fule," they saith. " He daun'
want you to stap'n, but us do. You mus'n
let the baal go between they poastis. You
mus' dap about a bit an' stap 'en gwain
droo."

" Aw ! " I says. " Why had'n 'ee told
me. But you want to speak to the feller
what kick 'en. 'Twas his fau't, nit mine."

With the zame, umpire blawed his wissle,
an' they started kickin' an' rishin' about
agean. Bim-bye I zeed wan of our chaps
go tearin' off wi'en in the oppozite direction,
an' arter a bit some other body gi'd 'en a
kick an' he went between the poastis up
tother end. I zeed the tother goldkeeper
jump about zix foot to try an' ketch 'en,
but he cude'n come to 'en.

Wull, then our vellers all holleyed out
" Gold," an' simmed very plaized wi'
theirzells. So then I beginned to see the
way o't. What you got fer to do is to try
fer to kick the ole baal in droo the gold-
poastis, an' the gold-keeper he've got to
stap 'ee.

" Haw, that's aisy," I thort to mezell.
" You let'n come down thees way agean."

Wull, twad'n very long avore I zeed the same feller comin' along like lightnin'. So I got raddy fer 'en.

" Look out, Jan," wan chap olleyed.

" I'm lookin'," I says.

So I stood where I considered the baal was commin' to an' held out me hands in raddiness. But the darn feller, 'staid o' kickin' the baal to me, as he shude a-done, he kick 'en clane across to another rid-an'-black chap tother side o' the gold, an' he titched 'en with his voot, an' o' cou'se, droo he went.

" Gold," they olleys agean, an' way-da-go, dalighted with theirzells.

" Yer, that id'n vair," I says. " I wad'n lookin' that way."

" Aw, you mus' be lookin' ev'ry way," says the captin.

" How many pairs of eyes be 'ee spaused to have on thees job ? " I says.

Arter that I did'n get a minute's paice. They was better vootballers, sim-so, than what our chaps was, an' they kep' comin' along an' tryin' to kick the baal droo my gold. Speshly thik li'l veller they caaled " inzide-out." A proper noosance, he was. An' he wad'n satisfied arter he'd done it wance. He mus' go back an' do it all ovver agean.

" Why daun' thik li'l chap zit down an' rest a bit," I says, " an' give some other body a chance ? "

" He played fer the Cristial Pallis wance," says the cap'm.

" Did 'er ? Wull, if he rinned about like he have to-day he desarved to have it," I said.

39

Presen'ly I zeed Maister Inzide-out comin' down agean wi' the baal, an' zame time I hap'm'd to nawtice his partner comin' along the opposite zide, an' lookin' turrable aiger.

"Ha!" thinks I to mezell. "I see what you'm on upon. You'm gwain to flip 'en across to the tother chap agean, but I'll be raddy fer 'ee this time."

An' zo I was. Wull—purty near. But nit quite. Drec'ly I zeed he was gwain to kick 'en, I dapped across to the tother gold-poast jist as the tother veller let go at the baal with his voot. O' cou'se, if I ad'n bin there twude a-bin a gold. An' I mid tell 'ee, I wished I was tain mile away. I did'n have time to putt up me hands, an' I stapped 'en with me vace. Bang! Man alive! 'Twas zacly like the kick of a mule.

Aw, my dear zaul. I never thort twude be a vace agean. I thort I'd bin hat by a zix-inch shell. I did'n knaw what 'ad ap'm'd. I cude'n zee an' I cude'n spaik, an' I cude'n braithe. I putt up wan hand to the back o' me haid to zee if me nawse had come out behind.

When me haid had stapped gwain around an' I got wan eye oppen, the cap'm come rinnin' up to me.

"Bravo, Jan," he says. "You stapped he butifle."

"Did I?" I says. "I thort p'raps I'd stapped a wizz-bang."

"Look out," he says. "They'm comin' agean."

"Be 'em?" I says. "Wull, you come an' putt your vace yer. I'm takin' mine 'ome."

An' zo I did.

Jan on the Revolving Staircase.

O' COU'SE, they women-volk and ole Tom Zalter was properly fallin' ovver theirzells to knaw what I do'd up to Lunnon, an' how I did get on.

"Tell us all the whole rigmarole an' pedigree, Jan," says Missis Snell, soon's ever the van had started.

"Better-way leave out the parts that id'n fit fer the young an' innocent," says Tom.

"Now, jis' you bide still, Tom Zalter, an' not keep on with they ole interferences," says Missis.

"Wull," I says "I'll tell 'ee es much as I can mind."

"And the rest you'll make up out of yer awn haid," says Tom.

"Why dissen hold thee baal, mump'aid?" says Missis Snell. "How is it you can't bide quiet two minutes together."

"I suppaus' 'tis because me mother was a wumman," says Tom.

"I shude think both yer mother an' yer vather, too, must a-bin mill-clappers. Get vore wai't, Jan, avore he gives me back a chicky answer."

"Wull," I says, "I was a bit nervous about gwain up to Lunnon all by mezell, you mid depaind. The passen let me have the name of a hotel where I must go to.

Wraut it down on a bit of a ticket he did, an' give me all paticlers how to get there. He's a rare chap, passen is, to help anybody out of trouble."

" Or into it," says Tom.

" You never knawed passen help anybody into trouble," I says.

" What about when he married me to my missis ? "

" On with your ole yap again, ban' 'ee ? " says Missis Snell. " What a terrifying toad you be."

" However, I thought to mezell, 'I've got a English tong in me haid, if tid'n quite the sort of a wan they uses up in Lunnon. 'Tis a pity if I can't find me way about.' "

" So off I goes.

" But arter that, mind you, 'tis a mazin' queer sinsation fer a ole contry chap like me to find hissell in Lunnon all alone by hissell.

" When I got out there to Paddyton Station I was like a man a-lost.

" So I went up to a policeman, which mother had impressed on me I must orwiz do up in Lunnon, an' I shawed 'en the ticket with the directions on it where the passen said I shude go to

" 'Aw,' the policeman says, 'you want to go underground.'

" 'I daun' want to do no-jis thing,' sort,' I saith. 'I ban't a rabbit.'

" Caw ! Did'n he laaf !

"'Undergroun' railway,' he saith. 'Down thikky drangways an' turn to the lef'.'

"Wull, so I did. But laur' bless 'ee, there simmed to be a dizzen differnt ways a body cude go, an' I was very soon in a proper ole bewilderness. I beginned to wish I had'n bin so fulish as to go to Lunnon by mezell. 'Very fule I shall look,' I thort 'if I gets into sitch a confusion that I can't extracticate mezell.'

"However, I axed another body an' he told me to go down the resolvin' staircase. Wull, o' cou'se, I did'n knaw what the resolvin' staircase was like, no more'n Adam, but I soon found out. They ban't a bit like ordnery stairs. They looks like 'em, first glimpse. But you daun' move yer veet when you'm gwain up or down. You keeps yer veet quite still, an' 'tis the stairs moves up or down an' takes 'ee which way you want to go."

"Yer, stiddy on," says Missis Endycott, "What do 'ee take us fer, I winder. You muzzen think jus' because you've bin up to Lunnon you can make us believe any ole witpot."

"Believe it or not," I says. "But what I'm tellin' you is gospel. I tell 'ee they stairs is orwiz on the move."

"Aw, 'tis right nuff," says Tom. "I knaw 'tis right cuz I've zeed our stairs home do the very same thing. I mind when Jane Tolley's darter was married an' I went ovver there in the aiv'min to the weddin'-party. When I got home, bout o' dree o'clock, there was the stairs gwain around like the ole 'obby-'osses to Barley-come Fair. Jis' like you say, Jan."

"I 'ad'n bin to no weddin'-party," I says. "An' my case wad'n same as yours. With you the furniture an' all was rinnin' around."

"That's right, Jan. I be dalled if 'tid'n

43

right. Cuz I knaws there was a baggarin'
chair there stood up agin the wall. An'
ev'ry time I went to zit on thikky chair the
li'l toad 'ud go cou'sin' off ha'f-ways
around the rume, an' down I'd go on the
floor a buster. An' bevore I cude get up
he'd flip back an' hat me a kick in the
niddick."

"I tell 'ee," I saith, "that thase-yer
staps is orwis gwain around, wan lot
upperds an' tother lot down'erds. Wance
you'm stood on the fust stap you've no
'casion to move yer veet. The same stap
that you'm stood on up the top takes 'ee
right down the bottom an' vicer-versy, an'
all the other staps is rinnin' along in front
or comin' along behind. An' a turrable
high staircase 'tis, too. 'Twude make 'ee
proper tired the ordnery way.'

"An' you say you zeed this with yer
awn eyes?" says Missis Endycott.

"Zeed it? Laur bless the wumman,
daun' I tell 'ee I had a ride down upon it.
Do 'ee think I draimed about it, or w'at?"

"Dalled if I knaws what to think 'ardly,"
her saith.

"I shude be frightened to death," says
Missis Snell. "Suppausin' they was to go
down all to wance instaid of one to a time?"

"Why, you'd get there all the quicker
fer that," says Tom.

"'Tis orright wance you'm on," I says.
"'Tis a bit ticklish gettin' on the fust time,
though 'tis aisy when you gets the nick
o't. There's a bit of a smooth place rinnin'
along on the ground, an' you staps on to
he, an' then, o' cou'se you'm rinnin' along
too. Wull, that carr's 'ee vore to the tap

44

o' the staps. An' natterally, you up's with yer voot to putt'n down the fust stap. But lo an' behold, bevore you can putt'n down you discovers that the tother voot which you'm standin' top of, is wan stap down a'raddy.

"An' while you'm lookin' at'n, an' winderin' how the jooce he come there, he'm two staps down. An' bevore you knaws what you'm doin' he's dree, an' vower. An', by jo, when you looks around to see what have hapm'd, darn'ee, you'm a dizzen staps from the tap. An' you ab'm moved! An' bless yer 'art, if you putts yer bag down 'pon the stap behind 'ee, he cometh down, too. He volleys 'ee down, wan stap behind 'ee all the way, genst you gets to the bottom.

"But I was gwain to tell 'ee 'bout when you comes to the bottom. That's where I got into a proper ole hobble, 'sure nuff.

"O' cou'se you must understand, when you'm down bottom o' the resolvin' stair-case it rins along the flat again like it do to the tap. An' you've got to dap off sideways.

"I was jis thinkin' to mezell, 'I 'op to gudeness I shall be abble to get off orright' when I zeed a gurt notice sticked up:

"'Stap off wi' the RIGHT voot.'

"Wull now, I knawed very well that was wrong, cuz I larned all about stappin' off when I was in the Home Defenders. 'Tid'n very much I did larn to be sure, cuz my ole haid wude'n hold it all. But wan thing I did knaw fer certain, an' that is, you must orwiz stap off wi' the LEFT voot. Caw, bless my zaul, did'n Colonel Brown an' the ole drill sargent spend days an' wiks knackin' that into our haids? Ha'f the trouble us did get into was because us wude verget an' stap off wi' the right voot. An' then they wude caal us but ev'rything.

" 'When be I gwain to larn 'ee orwiz to stap off wi' the lef' voot?' That's what the ole sargent use to zay. Said it to me scores o' times, he have.

" So I knawed thikky notice was all wrong. An' I pointed it out to a young vella what was tricklin' down the ole resolvin' staircase bezide me.

" 'You volks up in Lunnon dunnaw ev'rything, arter all,' I says. 'Us contry bumkins can larn 'ee zummat, I zee. You muzzen never stap off wi' the right voot. 'Tis all wrong. You mus' orwiz stap off wi' the lef' voot, an' if you daun' bleeve me you can ax Colonel Brown. He ort to knaw if anybody du. He've bin stappin' off all his life.'

" With the same I come to the smooth part down bottom, so I putt across me lef' voot an' stapped off in a proper manner.

" What hap'm'd arter that I can't axac'ly tell 'ee. Fer a minute I thought I was flippin' up they stairs again, back'ards. Then I zeed the station platform dap up in the air an' get hitched up in the ceilin; an' a hugly gurt weighin' machine took wan jump at me an' hat me along the floor.

" When I got up, the vella I'd bin tellin' to says, 'Thank 'ee very much fer shawin' me that. I've never tried to do it the proper way, but I will wan o' these days when I be tired o' life.' "

46

Jan on the Underground.

DID ever you try to travel about on thik ole underground railway, up to Lunnon?

I did wance. Never shall again, I 'op.

Why, laur bless 'ee, a fella need to be ha'f a rabbut only to vind his way about they ole stations. Zacly like a rabbuts berry they be. I çan't liken 'em to nort better. 'Tiz nothin' but a maze o' tunnels all ovver the place. Soon's ever you've got droo wan, an' thinks now you'm coming somewhere, there's a couple more bevore 'ee, wan gwain left-'anded an' wan gwain right-'anded. An' whichever you takes he sure to be wrong. By the time you've trapesed droo ha'f-a-dizzen tunnels you'm back where you started to.

Proper ole caper I had, sure 'nuff, to the ole underground station there to Paddyton. Rissell Square was the place I wanted to go to, cuz that was the directions the parson putt on the ticket he let me have.

So far as I cude zee I had all-so-gude a chance to get to Jericho as what I had to Rissel Square.

The times I rinned up an' down they ole tunnels lookin' fir a train! And my ole bags an' parcels was like a ton weight.

I wad'n no better off if I axed anybody the way to go. They was all coosin' along

47

at sitch a paze that you was foce'd to rin alongside while you was axing 'em. An' wi' my quantity o' luggage I wad'n abble to keep up the paze 'long 'nuff to ketch the answer.

"Which is the way to Rissell Square, plaize?" I axed wan chap. Stood right in the way o'n, I did, so's he'd be fo'ced to stap a bit. But the baggarin' toad rinned all out around me an' was off again like a long-dog.

"Change to Piccalilly Circus," I yerd'n say, just as he was disappearin' down a tunnel.

"Change to Piccalilly Circus!" I saith. "I wish to gudeness I cude change to a ferret an' then I mid stand chance to vind me way about theese-yer rabbut holes."

So then I axed another chap, an' he says, "You wants Bakerloo."

"Who's he?" I says. But he was gone. Down a tunnel.

However, I thort to mezell, "'Bakerloo,' he said. I'll mind he. I'll vind ole Bakerloo some'ow, an' zee what he've got to zay about it."

So the nex' chap I zeed I says, "Where's Bakerloo to?"

"Down the staps." An' off *he* goes. Down a tunnel.

"Thank 'ee sure," I says. "I've bin up an' down a vew thousan' staps. A hunderd or two more waun' make much odds."

However, 'twad'n very long bevore I zeed a big notice sticked up agin the wall, "Bakerloo," and a finger sticked out showin' 'ee which way to go.

48

"Us be gettin' on," I says. "I mid get there now avore I dies of old age."

So then I come to a chap in brassen buttons stood to a gate.

"Ticket," he saith.

"Thanky, sure," I saith, an' putt out me hand vor'n.

"Where's yer ticket to?" he saith. Very short he was with it, too.

"Daun' you be vunny," I says. "You ab'm let me have wan not 'eet."

I thought thik vella was gwain to say summat rude fer a minute. I cude zee it tryin' to come out of his face but it cude'n find his mouth, sem-so. Then I spause he zeed I wad'n proper way-wise, so he tole me to go back an' get a ticket to the bookin' orfis.

"That's right," I says. "You zend me back into they ole tunnels again, an' I'll be rinnin' around fer the rest o' the wik."

Caw, that made'n laaf. But he took pity on me an' showed me where to get me ticket to, an' when I come back he knacked a bit out of 'en with a pair o' pinchers an' let me go down on to the platvorm.

There was scores an' hunderds o' volks there waitin', so I put me bag an' parcels down on the floor, an' all of a sudden I yerd a jooce of a racket an' I zeed a funny li'l train comin' out of a hole.

I knawed there was gwain to be a bit of a scummer with so many volks tryin' to push on all to wance, so I thort I'd wait a bit an' get in aisy. But lo an' behold bevore I had time to turn around I'm baggered if he wad'n off again into another hole up tother end.

49

So I goes up to a porter chap.

"Thik train id'n gone, is 'er?"

"Can't zee 'en about no-place," he saith.

"But I got to ride in he," I says.

"You'll have to make'ase, then," he saith. "If you'm quick you mid ketch 'en comin' back."

"Don't none of 'em bide no longer than that?" I says. "Why, down our way they staps quatter-nower sometimes."

"I dersay," he saith. "But you zee, thase-yer li'l places like Lunnon ban't important 'nuff fer that."

With the same along comes another train, so this time I tried to squaise in wi' the rest. But I tooked up so much room with me gurt bag and they ole parcels that ev'rybody was pushin' bevore me, an' I was all the time gettin' vurder away.

However, the porter chap olleyed to me, "Come on, dad," an' he bundled me in neck an' crop, chucked in me bag an' parcels arter me, putt fast the door, gived his ole train a shove, an' off us went with a jit that knacked my haid bang up agin the wall.

"If this is travellin' in Lunnon," thinks I to mezell "then give me the ole carrier's van."

However, I was in, an' me next trouble was, how was I gwain to get out? I was feared to death lest I shude go past the place an' never know it. Ev'ry station us come to a fella poked in his haid an' holleyed out summat. But what he said, I cude'n make out, no more'n if it had bin French or Double Dutch.

Ev'ry time he 'olleyed summat I had to

ax the chap next to me, " What did 'er zay ? " And ha'f the time I did'n knaw what 'twas arter he'd repaited it.

So I says to 'en, " Wude you plaise to let me knaw when us comes to Picallily Circus ? "

" Nex' station," he says. An' the words wad'n hardly out of his mouthe avore us flipped into the station an' come to a stan'still.

" This is Picalilly Circus," he saith.

Caw, darn 'ee ! 'Twas bad 'nuff gettin' in. But 'twas a sight wiss gettin' out. What a skimpy li'l time they bides to a station. I wad'n properly prepared for't, as you mid say, an' I had all the works in the world to gather together my parcels. Everybody's legs seemed to be in the road. 'Twas all the winders in the world I wad'n carried on to the nex' station. You see, I wad'n hardly dapper enough to squaise out along o' the fust party, an' by the time I'd picked up all me belongings the new lot was pushin' in. So I was in a proper quandairy, sure 'nuff.

An' by Jo, soon's ever the last o' that lot was in the train the station-master chap was fer shuttin' the door an' shovin' the ole train along. So I 'olleyed to 'en :

" Yer," I says. " Nit so vast, me ole buck. I wants to get out."

" Come on, father," he saith. " Where have 'ee bin to ? In under the sate ? "

" I ban't yer father," I says. " If I had a-bin I should have larned 'ee behaviour."

An' more I shude a-said to 'en, fer I veeled like it. But he pushed along his ole train an' away-da-go.

So there I was to Picalilly Circus. The only pickles I cude zee was the one I was in mezell. 'Twas all they ole tunnels ovver again. However, I managed to vind the proper train and to-last I got to this-yer ole Rissell Square place.

Wad'n I some thankful when I got out o' the train! "Now," I says, "I shall zoon get some fresh air in me inzide." So I went along where it said "Way out," an' I passed out droo the geat where a chap took me ticket.

But laur bless yer 'art, I wad'n out 't all. Tell about "Way out!" 'Twas the way in! I was inzide a gurt ole cage along with a score or two more volk. 'Pon me zaul if it had bin back to the ole Picalilly Circus I shude a-said us was in the monkey-house.

Us was like herrins in a box. "If many more comes in," I says to mezell, "summat will have to go fer certin."

An' with the same summat went.

What hap'm'd I dunnaw axac'ly. All of a sudden I veeled me hair gwain' up droo me hat, an' I zeed the walls gwain' down droo the floor. Then I discovered us was all gwain up in the air. Bim-bye us finished with a pop, the geat oppened of his own accord, I scammelled arter me bag an' parcels, an' somebody pushed me out into the street.

Jan Finds a Hotel.

SEEMING to me a feller's troubles is never over when he's up in Lunnon.

As fast as he gets out o' wan quandairy he'm into another. An' that's the candid truth, begad.

When they bumped me out from the old lift into the street at the underground railway station, I stood there like a fule frightened. I did'n know no more'n a gawk which way to go.

However, I'd got the derections of the hotel where I'd got to go to. The passen had wraut down the derections on a bit of a ticket. "Imperial Hotel, Rissell Square," that's what it said on the ticket. Passen let me have he bevore I come away from home, cuz he said 'twas a very nice place fer me to go to, an' the place where he orwiz went to hissell. So I reckoned if 'twas gude nuff fer passen 'twas gude nuff fer me.

So I showed this-yer ticket to a policeman an' axed 'en if he knawed any sitch place. 'Tis winderfle what they policemen do know, 'pon me zaul. He putt me in the way o't in a minute.

"Second turnin' on the left," he saith. An' I be darned if he wad'n right begad. I turned around the second to the left, an' there was a monstrous gurt place, sure nuff, an' "Imperial Hotel" wraut up ovver the door in gurt letters a voot long. I

53

knawed derec'ly I'd come to the right place, when I zeed "Imperial Hotel" sticked up ovver the door, cuz 'twas exac'ly what the passen wraut down on the ticket he let me have bevore I left ·Muddlecome. I compared the two, an' 'twas exac'ly right to a letter.

What it is to be educative.

But laur, bless 'ee cheel, I was proper frightened to zee the place. I was reely. 'Twas like a king's palace. Whatever do 'em erec' sitch gurt places fer ?

"If I wance gets properly inzide o' thikky place," I thought to mezell, "I shall get lost fer certin. Can't help but get lost."

You had to go up dree or vower long stonen staps to get up to the vore door. What they wants stitch gurt doors fer I can't imagine. There never wad'n anybody that size fer certin. An' why do 'em have two doors instead o' wan, unless 'tis wan to go in an' tother to come out.

However, thinks I to mezell, they can't eat me fer certin. So up I goes up they stonen staps with me gurt bag an' me parcels. An' I was jis gwain to oppen the vore door ; in fac', I set down me bag an' was raichin' out me hand for the same purpose, when a feller pulled 'en oppen from the inzide. Wull, o' cou'se, I thought he was wanting to come out, so I stapped back a bit to make way fer 'en. But he did'n make no attempt to come out, an' there he stood with the hannle o' the door to his hand, bowin' an' scrapin' like a Punch an' Judy show.

So to-last I says, " Be you comin' out,"

I says, " or no ? Cuz if you ban't I shude like to come in."

Wull, all he said was to go on bowin', so I up's with me bag an' strakes past 'en. I thought he was some sort of a officer chap with his brassen buttons. But I discovered arterwads that he was putt there same purpose to oppen the door fer volks comin' in.

Lunnon's a winderfle place, sure 'nuff. Fancy keepin' a chap in brassen buttons to oppen the door fer ole Jan Stewer.

However, I wad'n very much better off now I was inzide, fer I did'n knaw what to do ner where to go to. There was heaps o' volks about, cuz they kep' fallin' ovver my parcels in all derections. But fer the life o' me I did'n knaw which belonged to the place ner which the place belonged to.

However, I reckoned the door-oppener chap wude knaw zummat about it. So I goes up to he an' I says, " Bagging yer pardon, zur," I says, " can you tell me if there's a spare bed in the place where a chap cude sleep to-night ? "

" I cude'n tell 'ee," he saith. " But if you inquire o' the young lady in the office her knaw'th all about it."

Well, I did'n think very much o' that caper. Between you an' me an' the geat-post it did'n seem 'ardly the sort of thing to discuss with a young lady you'd never zeed bevore in your life.

However, I did'n zee no other hope ver't, so I went ovver to the little place where her could look out droo the winder, an' I wished her gude arternune.

Her was a nice, affable maid, sure 'nuff,

an' her did'n sim to objec' to my spaikin' to her the laistest bit in the world. Her wish me " Gude arternoon " as if us had knawed wan tother fer years.

But I was properly nervous an' did'n 'ardly knaw how to broach sitch a subjic', an' I be darned if I did'n make a proper fule o' mezell. What's think I said ?

I said, " Plaise to excuse me, my dear, but can I bide yer all night ? "

O' cou'se, her took me up in a minute.

" You can if you wish it," her saith. " But would'n 'ee sooner sit down sometimes ? "

Cou'se, I zeed derec'ly what a stoobid remark I'd made. An' us had a gude laaf, both of us. Her laafed, an' so I did, too. An' arter that us got on like a houze avire. 'Tis winderfle how a gude laaf will break the ice as the saying is. You might veel strange with a body fer a wik. But if you haves a gude laaf together you'm friendly in vive minutes.

" Did you want a bedrume ? " her saith.

" Yes, plaise, my dear," I says, " if you got wan to spare. I've brought me awn nightshirt," I said, " an' brish an' comb, an' ev'rything I shall require in a manner o' spaikin'. I awnly wants a bed ; an' my wife impressed upon me I was to ax 'ee plaise to be sure an' zee he was properly aired."

Wull, then her laafed again. I dersay her guessed I was come up from the contry. They can tell. You mid depend they can tell. But her was very considerate to me all the same. Her did'n sim to matter how much trouble her took. Proper nice

56

maid her was, sure 'nuff, an' I promised
I'd zend her back a pound o' crame soon's
ever I got home to Deb'mshur. An' I did,
too, an' had to make a doost of a lot of
explanations to the missis.

Well, the young lady said her cude spare
me a bedrume orright. But laur' bless 'ee,
what a parcel of ole vorms an' sarrymonies
there was to go droo to be sure.

Cou'se I'm tellin' now 'bout the time the
war was on.

Fust of all her let me have a bit of a
dockyment which her told me to full in.

" What's this," I says, " a dog lishence ? "

" That's fer yer nationality," her saith.

" I daun' want none," I says. " All I
wants is a bed fer the night an' a bit o'
brexis in the mornin'. I daun' require
none o' they ole fanciful itums."

Caw ! Then her laafed more'n ever. I
reckon her must a-thort I was a quare ole
card.

" 'Tid'n nothin' to eat," her saith.
" Since the war bin on ev'rybody must putt
down their nationality to avoid taking in
German spies."

" Laur bless yer zaul, my dear," I said.
" You needn't be feared o' that. I ab'm
got sainse 'nuff to be a spy. I be only ole
Jan Stewer, from Muddlecome. I shude'n
know the way to be a spy if you was to
offer me a thousan' pound."

" I'm sure you wude'n try," her saith.
" But ev'rybody has to full in wan o' they
papers, if he was Archbishop o' Canter-
bury."

" You plaize to give me instructions
what to putt down, miss," I says. " I

ban't much in the custom o' gwain about to these places."

" 'Tis quite zimple," her saith. " Jis' putt yer name down there, looky. Now, what's yer nationality ? "

" Wull," I says, " I've orwiz attended church so long ago as I can mind, an' that's where I was baptised to. But I've bin to chapel manys-a-times, although I ban't methody, arter that."

Caw, then her laafed again. I shude think her must a-bin very glad I come, for her was gettin' plenty o' merriment, seem-so.

" You daun' understand," her saith. " Nationality is meaning what contry you belongs to. What contryman be 'ee ? "

" Deb'm."

" No, no," her says. " Deb'm id'n a contry."

" Bes' contry in the world," I says, an' purty smart, too. I wad'n gwain to have no Lunnon cockney puttin' up his ole roves of houses bevore Deb'm.

" Bes' contry in the world," I says, " either fer mait, drink, men or maids ; although it mus' be pretty gude contry turned you out."

I thought I'd better-way putt in that li'l bit, cuz if her was to get narked her cude make it very ockerd fer me.

But her wad'n the laist bit putt out o' the way. Her aunly laafed again. I never zeed sitch a maid to laaf in all my days.

" I suppose if you'm Deb'm you'm British," her saith.

" My dear cheel," I says. " Did'n they larn 'ee histry when you went to skule ?

Why, if there had'n been no Deb'ms there would'n a-bin no British."

" Well," her saith. " You putt down British on the paaper an' you'll be orright."

So I putt down British to plaise the maid. But I reckon it should a-bin Deb'm by gude rights.

So then her oppened a gurt buke an' rinned her vinger down ovver the list. An' then her wraut down a vigger on a bit of a card and let me have. I've got 'en home now. cuz I keeps 'en for what they calls a cheffoneer.

" Room number vive hunderd an' twenty wan," her saith.

" Gude laur," I saith. " Hab'm 'ee got wan handier than that ? He sounds a turrable long way off."

But he wad'n.

Her putt her vinger to wan o' they li'l nubs that rings bells, an' up come a chap they called Boots, cuz he'd got on shoes. Must a-come up droo the floor, I should think.

" Vive, two, wan," her said.

An' with the same he wips up my bag, sticks a parcel under each arm, hung two or dree round his neck, balanced a couple on his nose (or that's what it seemed like to me), daps into the ole lift, me arter his tail, up us goes in the air, then flips out again, licks along a drangway into a room, " Vive, two, wan," he says, an' disappears back droo the floor where he come from.

An' then I drayed me breath.

The Ever Opening Door.

I TELL 'ee what, now. Twude'n take very long fer me to bide up there to Lunnon bevore I shude go clane off me haid. An' that's wai'out a word of a lai.

Caw dally, you'm on the op-skip-an-jump from mornen to night. I prefers takin' things a bit more leisurable than what that is. Seemin' to me vokes in Lunnon never id'n content wai what they'm on upon now. They mus' be all the time vidgetin' about what they'm gwain to do nex'. They daun' take no delight to zit down quiet an' comferable fer a nower an' tell a bit. They must be orwiz dappin' about vrom wan ole kickshaw to another like a passel o' grass-'oppers.

An' what howers they do go to bed! They never gets no buty sleep fer certin, an' gudeness knaws they wants it bad 'nuff, zome o'm.

Wad'n I some tired when I went up-ovver to bed thik fus' night in the ole hotel I zee now why they wants they ole lifts about. Nobody ab'm got sproil left to lop up auver stairs when comes bed-time. Or what they calls bed-time. I shude call it purt' near gettin'-up time, mezel'.

I knaw wan thing. When I waked up nex' mornin' I cude'n think fer the life o' me where I was to. I gappid all around the rume, an' bother me if I cude size it up

60

't all. O' cou'se, 'twas all strange-like to me, an' I beginned to winder whe'er the pixies had'n carr'd me off or no.

An' the dayslight was straimin' in droo the winder 'nuff to dazzle anybody.

Thinks I to mezell, " Whatever time can it be fer gudeness sake ? "

So I tooked out me watch from in under the piller, an' 'twas upright zeb'm.

Mai dear days ! Zeb'm o'clock an' no cows fetched in, no 'osses tended to, ner nort. Ha'f the mornin' gone an' nothin' done, an' me lied in bed. I dapped out o' bed quicker'n I'd done fer years.

An' then o' cou'se it all come back home to me where I was to, an' I remembered that there wad'n no cows, ner pigs, ner poultry, ner nothin' to zee to. But how I come to lie a-bed to that hower I cude'n think. 'Twas poking about to sitch redecklus time the night avore. That's what done it.

" Caw," says I to mezell, " whatever will 'em think o' me comin' down to brexis this time o' day ? 'Twill be vornunes-time genst I be properly dressed.

Wull, an' o' cou'se, me not bein' way-wise as the sayin' is, as regards to hotels, I cude'n think fer the life o' me how I was gwain to get dressed. Fer wan thing I had'n the laistest idea where the pump was to. So how was I gwain to waish fer a start ? An' where cude I get a drap o' hot watter to shavy ? I tell 'ee straight, I beginned to wish I was back home 'long o' mother, where I cude holley down ovver the stairs fer anything I wanted. Most mortal

61

lonesome I did veel, sure 'nuff. Plenty o' granjer an' no pump.

However, arter a minute or two I zeed a soort of a basin thing sticked agin the wall. I thought he'd do vine to waish in, but I cude'n zee no watter-jug no-place. Bim-by I noticed there was taps ovver this-yer basin to turn around. So I turned wan around to zee if any watter wude come.

Caw! My stars! What a shout I did let out, to be sure. Must a-yerd me down Muddlecome, I shude think. The watter come, right 'nuff. 'Twas scaal-'ot! An' I'd got the tother hand in under. Then I zeed the word " Hot " pon-top the ole tap, an' I knawed 'twas true, begad.

But whoever wude think of havin' boilin' 'ot watter in yer bedrume, only by turnin' a tap!

However, 'tis very convaynient, an' nobody can't say no other. An' I was abble to shavy an' ev'rything, an' never mind about no pump.

Wull, arter I'd made mezell look proper viddy, I went along to the ole lift, for I'd got into the way o't by this time. Although, arter that, I never got what you mid call proper reconciled to thik ole contraption, cuz I orwiz use to think suppausin' zummat was to give way an' the whole bag o' thicks was to go haidlong.

Well there, it never did'n, thanks be.

'Twas gone eight o'clock when I got downstairs, or down lift, or whatever's the proper way to term it. Darn if I wad'n ha'f ashamed to look anybody in the vace, I was railly. An' I did'n expec' no other but what all the brexis wude be eat, an' none left. However, I zeed my ole friend the Butes an' I says to he, " Baggin' yer pardon," I says, " is all the brexis done away ? "

" Done ! " he says. " Why, 'tis only eight o'clock."

" Eight ! " I says. " Whatever time do vokes go to work up yer about ? "

He did'n zeem to knaw what to make o' that hardly, so I axed 'en which was the way to the kitchen.

" Kitchen ? " he zaith. " What do 'ee want kitchen fer ? "

" What fer ? " I says. " I wants me brexis, o' cou'se. Did 'ee think I wanted me 'air cut ? "

" Brexis rume straight in droo on the right," he zaith.

Cou'se I did'n knaw they'd got a special rume fer brexis, an' I told 'en I was quite willin' to go in kitchen if 'twude zave any work clainin' up.

But he did'n zeem to understand my maining. I daun' reckon they'm too yark be-arf, not the Lunnon volk. They makes out that we contry volk is a bit zauft, but I zim the Lunnoners can be a bit slaw zometimes.

However, I volleyed his derections, an' I thought if they was minded fer me to bissle up the bes' parler 'twas their awn look-out. So off I strakes, an' I come to the place where he said.

An' then I be darned if I did'n have another ole scare, begad. 'Pon me zaul, when you come to consider the times I was gallied 'most out o' me wits 'tis a winder I ever come back alive to tell the tale.

63

As I zaid bevore, I come to this-yer door to go into the brexis place, an' I was jis' 'pon the point to putt out me hand to push 'en opp'n, when the darn thing begin to opp'n by hizzell.

Well, o' cou'se, I considered there mus' be zome other body tother zide wanting to come out. So I dap wan-zide to let' en pass. An' with the zame the blimmin' door shut to agean.

"Wull," thinks I to mezell, "that's mortle quare. Zomebody must a-oppened the ole door, that's fer certin, an' 'twad'n me fer I never titch 'en." So I goes vore wance more to push 'en opp'n, an' be dalled if he did'n do zame agean. Bevore ever I cude reach me hand to the hannle he starts to opp'n of his awn accoord. An' there wad'n nobody there to come out, that was the funny part o't, cuz I cude zee there wad'n. Doors was wide opp'n an' nobody there. Nit a zaul.

I beginned to winder whe'er the place was troublezome or no, or whe'er I was draimin'. However, I did'n zee no sainse in biding there all day, so I strakes in droo, an' wad'n no zooner inzide than the darn ole doors closed theirzells.

So I got me brexis, an' very gude 'twas, too. But laur, tell about bein' laate! I was wan o' the early burds accordin' to their way o' reck'ning. An' when I'd most finished there was still volks trapesin' in as though 'twas fus' thing in the mornen, instead of purt' near middle day.

An' when I got up to lef' the rume, if you'll believe me they darned ole doors played up the zame caper again. Soon's

64

ever I come nigh 'em they beginned to
opp'n. Never titch'n I did'n, an' never
zaid a wurd to 'em. They opp'n their awn
zel!

" Whatever's come to the blimmin' ole
door?" I zaid. " Have he got eyes?
Can he zee me comin'?"

I did'n knaw I zaid it out loud. But I
must a-done cuz a gen'lman behine me give
a bit of a laaf.

" 'Tis a patent soort of a door," he zaith.
" When you putts yer weight 'pon the mat,
the doors opp'ns."

An' I'm popped if 'twad'n true, cheel!
Cuz I tried it ever zo many times to prove
it. When I stood tap the mat the double
doors opp'n theirzels, an' drec'ly I stap
back off the mat they shut together again.
How 'tis done I can't tell 'ee, ner I shude'n
a-believed it if I 'ad'n zeed it with me awn
eyes.

Wull, wull, they'm winderfle volks up in
Lunnon fer saving theirzel's work. Only
to fancy wantin' a paatent to opp'n the
door vor 'em! I suppause nex' thing
they'll have a machine to blaw their
nawses.

Home.

(Soliloquy of Jan Stewer on arriving home in a snowstorm, November, 1919, from military service in Egypt.)

HOME!
   Home, begad.
   'Tis snawin', an' blawin', an' freezin', an' I be sneezin' an' barkin', an' me nawse gets nipped off if I aunly putts 'en outzide the door, an' the sky is as black as thinder, an' ev'rything in the shops is as dear as zuvrins, an' they voretells 'tis gwain to be the wist winter o' the lot, but 'tis HOME, an' that's all I cares about fer the present.

   I've left the warm zin behine me fer a bit, zim-zo, an' I mus' zay I veels the cold most jewsive. If I aunly goes two enches away from the vire the ole gewze-vlesh creeps up all ovver me, an' me knees is knackin' together, an' me teeth is chitterin'.

   But 'tis Home.

   An' there's other kinds of warmness bezides the yet o' the zin. There's the zight o' yer awn volks ; an' the ole familiar noises which you never did'n use to take no notice of, but now they makes 'ee preck up yer yers like music.

   There's the squaik o' the geat, an' the grint o' the ole zow out in coort, an' mother sissin' the cat out from the dairy, an' Jane upstairs zinging to her work, an' the cockerells holleyin' across to Varmer Urferd's that maister have a-come 'ome. An' there's the li'l ole robin ridbress knackin' up agin the winder, an' the chillern outzide spaikin' English.

Ees. An' there's the hills an' the green vields an' the trees an' haidges, instaid o' the long ole miles o' flat zand out to Egyp'.

Aw, ees ! 'Tis HOME. An' 'tis DEB'M. An' it makes 'ee veel a zort o' warm inzide, although the outzide of 'ee is shivverin'.

Lias Buzzacott's Two Ounces

(An incident of the severe rationing during a period of the Great War, when caterers were permitted to serve no more than two ounces of flour in any form to each consumer at the afternoon meal).

IF you cude a-yeard poor ole Lias Buzzacott tell this-yer yarn you'd a-split yer zides. Darn if twude'n make a cat laaf.

'Twas in the ole Carrier's Van he told it, an' he'm a dry ole toad best o' times. Proper dry ole toad he is.

"So you was had fer wance, then, Lias?" says Missis Snell. "'Tis gude to see you took in sometimes. You'm so fond of havin' other folks on, an' makin' 'em look fulish. Now you knaws what 'tis like yerzell."

"Tell us all the whole rigmarole, Lias," says Missis Endycott. "What was you doin' gallivantin' about in that manner at all fer, I shude like to knaw?"

"Wull, 'twas like this-yer, missis. Me an' a young lady——"

"You an' a what?" says Missis Snell.

"Aw," says Missis Endycott, "so there was a young lady as well, was there?"

"Cou'se there was," says Lias. "What's think?"

"Do you yer what Lias is tellin' about, Jan Stewer?" says Missis Snell. "Ban't you surprised at 'en?"

"No-ti-no," I says. "I'm surprised at the young lady, that's all. Shows her 'ad'n got very much taste."

"Aw, you'm only jellis," says Lias. "She was a proper nice young lady, I can tell 'ee."

"She must be turrable short-sighted," says Tom, "to take up with you."

"She wude need to be turrable long-sighted to zee ort in you worth takin' up with," says Lias.

"Better-way tell us all about it, Lias," says Missis Snell, "an' then us can jidge fer ourzells. What was it you was so upsot about?"

"Why, this-yer food economy caper. I didn' knaw nort about sitch thing. It come on me like a flash o' thinder, as the sayin' is.

"You zee, 'twas like this-yer. I've bin away, stappin', as you do knaw along o' some relations. Very nice folks they be, but I ban't gwain to tell 'ee jis zacly where I bin to, else you'll knaw as much as what I do, an' that wude be a pity, sure nuff.

"However, I mid tell 'ee that there's a very nice maiden to this-yer place, a sort of a off-relation o' mine. I never seed the maid avore, but us got on very well together none the more fer that. O' cou'se, you folks what sees me ev'ry day, as the sayin' is, you dunnaw what a gude-lookin' chap

69

I be when I be waished an' properly spruced up fer the occasion.

" Be-as-twill, us got vore very well wai' wan tother, an' wan day I up an' axed her whe'er her wude'n like to go along o' me fer a bit of a walk. An' her said her wude. Proper jumped to the chance, her did, which shaws that her's got more preception, in a manner o' spaikin', than what some of 'ee has out yer.

" So her preposed that her shude take me into the town fer a walk, and shaw me all the vamous places there was to be seed.

" So off us started, and 'twas a butifle day, so us had a lovely walk."

" What did 'ee tell about all the time, Lias ? " says Missis Snell.

" Aw, 'bout the weather, missis," says Lias. " Fust I said it was hot, an' her said 'ees 'twas, an' then nex' time her said 'twas hot, an' I said 'ees 'twas. An' so us kep' on takin' turn about like that."

" I knawed I shude get a lie told me when I axed 'ee," says Missis.

" Why did 'ee ax me fer, then ? "

" Git along with thee tale, mump'aid."

" Wull, bim-bye, arter us had looked to all there was to see, an' got tired o' sayin' 'twas 'ot, I beginned to veel a bit leery, 'cus to tell 'ee the truth I 'ad'n 'ad very much of a dinner being that excited to think that I was gwain out to walk with a purty maid."

" Her must a-bin a big lump of a maid to take away your appetite," says Tom.

" Her was the mos' ansum figger you ever seed," said Lias.

" Never mind about the figger of her,"
says Missis. " Get on with yer ole yarn."

" Wull, as I tells 'ee, I was properly
hungerd, not being wan o' the soort that
cude live on love. So I says to the maid,
'Wude'n you like a cup o' tay ?' an' her
says, 'Ees, I wude.' "

" She wad'n backward 't all," says Tom.

" No, she wad'n nothin' backward. Nit
ha'f so backward as what I was.

" Wull, o' cou'se, I axed her where she
wude like fer to go. If I'd a-bin by mezell
I shude a-went into a public-houze an' had
a glass o' beer an' a bit o' braid an' chaise.
But, o' cou'se, I cude'n invite the maid to
do that. So her said her knawed a very
nice caffy where us cude get tay to. I
did'n know nort about no caffys, so I said,
'Orright, miss, you laid the way.' So us
come to this-yer place, an' 'twas wan o'
they swell consarns where you sits down to
a tittie li'l taable with a bit of a tablecloth
like a pocket-ancher which they putts on
all skew-wiff, an' a bunch o' vlowers in the
middle, an' haves a dinky li'l cup about the
size o' yer thumb. There was a passel o'
chaps with their maidens sot about to the
different tables, gaapin' into wan tothers'
eyes, like a caalve lookin' droo a kay-'ole."

" An' I spause you did the same," said
missis.

" Tell 'ee the truth, Missis, I did'n knaw
where to look hardly. I veeled about as
comferable as a cow in a church. However,
a maid come to see what us wanted, an' I
said us wanted our tay. Her axed did us
want tay an' braid an' butter, an' I said

71

'ees. I'd a-said 'ees if her had axed wude us have bran-mash an' oil-cake.

"Be that as it may, her tooked along this yer tay an' braid an' butter. There was a li'l tom-tit of a tay-pot that I cude a-swallered, lid an' all, an' vower teeny-weeny bits o' braid an' butter, about as big as me two vingers. I cude have ait the whole lot in wan bite, an' that was fer the two o' us.

"Wull, the young lady had her two bits an' I had mine. I had to make two chaws o't fer the look o' the thing, as you mid say. But so-fer as me appetite was consarned I mid so well swallered a mouthe-ful o' wind.

"So when the maid what belonged to the place was passin' by I called her ovver an' says, 'Bring along some more braid an' butter, my dear, Full up a gude-size platter wai't.'

"'I be zorry,' her zaith, 'I can't let 'ee have no more.'

"'What do 'ee main ?' I says, 'I be willin' to pay fer't. I'll let 'ee have the money bevore'and if you think I be gwain to chait 'ee.'

"Laur days, did'n her laaf. 'Tid'n that,' her saith, 'but you ban't 'lowed no more'n two ounces o' braid. If us was to let 'ee have any more us wude be took up bevore the jidge.'

"'Two ounces,' I says. 'Laur a-massey, I wants two pound.'

"'You can't have no more'n two ounces,'' her says, 'not if you was the Laurd Mayor o' Lunnon. 'Tis the law o' the land.'

"The maid along with me her was properly shaking with laafin'.

" 'Did'n you knaw that ? ' her says.

" 'Knaw it ?' I saith, 'o' cou'se I did'n knaw it. If I had I'd a-took a hunk o' braid in me pocket.'

" 'Us cude'n let 'ee ait it yer, even if you did,' says the maid that belonged to the place. 'Us muzzen zee 'ee ait no more'n two ounces.'

" 'Laur', bless the maid,' I says. 'If I'd a-got ha'f a loaf yer you wude'n zee me ait it. I be that hungerd you'd never zee the gwain o't. Can I have a couple aigs ?' I says.

" 'Ees, you can have a couple aigs,' her says, 'but you'll be fo'ced to ait 'em wai'out braid, cus you've had yer two ounces.'

" 'Caw, darn the two ounces,' I says, 'Keepin' on about the ole two ounces. Why I cude putt they in me oller tooth. Wull, bring us along some caakes,' I says, 'us'll ha' to do the best us can wai' they.'

" 'I be very sorry,' her said. 'I can't let 'ee have no cakes nuther, cus you ban't allowed no more vlour. You zee, you ban't allowed but the two ounces o' vlour, an' if you haves it in the braid you can't have it in the caake. 'Tis owin' to the ole submarines what have sunk so many o' the ships.'

" 'Darn the maid,' I says, 'bring us along a blimmin' submarine then, an' I'll ait he. An' let's get back 'ome,' I says, 'avore I dies o' starvation. Two ounces ! 'Tis a insult to a feller's innerds.' "

Dancing.

HOW I come to be sitch a fule as to go to thik ole wiss-drive an' dance I dunnaw.

Wull that's a lai. I *do* knaw. 'Twas because my missis had a new dress ; that was the cause o't. If her had'n had thik new dress I don't suppause us wude a-went neast the place. Her'd had this-yer dress for wiks, but her had'n had no chance to shaw 'en off, seem-so.

So when the invite come for the ole wiss-drive an' dance her thought twude be a fus'rate opportunity to let Sarah Tolley an' wan or two more glimpse her new fal-de-dals.

Be-as-twill she decided we shude take an' go, so us took an' went.

Lot of ole trumpery I call 'twas when us got there, an' I veeled about as much at home as a cow to a weddin'. Too much ole formality fer me. I'd sooner have a party home in the bes' kitchen like us use to arter a day's rabbitin', when the women-volk an' the maidens dropped in an' George Cann tooked along his ole accorjon. Then us had dances that *was* dances, that a body cude understand an' join in, an' if us wanted a hand to cards all well an' gude. If you hapm'd to play a trump in the wrong place nobody odds it. Aunly laaf at 'ee.

But laur bless yer 'art, the ole wiss drive was more like a passel o' sawjers on parade. I was feared ev'ry time the ole bell wude

ring avore I'd vinished, an' it did'n give a
veller time to think what he was about of.
An' I'm darned if I cude vind whichy table
I'd got to go to ha'f the time, an' twude be
a proper ole confusion, me up wan end o'
the rume lookin' fer a place, an' the volks
up tother end all holleyin' vor me.

But there! Most times I'd only got to
bide to the same table, which mitigated a
lot of commotion.

I did'n win no prize. Wance or twice I
fancy I mid have got on purty well if I
had'n had no partner. But so sure as I
got middlin' gude cards I'd have ole Mother
Sparks fer a partner, or Missis Grinslade, or
Judy Weston. An' I'd defy anybody to
make tricks with they, unless he'd got all
the trumps.

Ole Judy let two tricks go baggin' wance,
an' her zot there with the ace in her hand
all same time. When I took her to tackle
about it her said her never liked playin'
the ace if her cude avoid it, cuz wance he
was gone you never cude'n get'n back
again. I suppause her tooked a delight in
lookin' to 'en.

Funny part o't was ole Judy tooked a
prize. I was properly frightened when I
yerd her name caaled out.

"Wat is it, the booby prize?" I said.

"No-ti-no," they said. "Her've got
third prize."

My dear days! If Judy did'n strake up
the room like the Laurd Mayor o' Lunnon,
zac'ly.

An' all the rest o' the eve'min her was
givin' ev'rybody instructions the way to
play wiss.

'Twad'n 'vore nex' day, when zomebody was lookin' down ovver her card again, they discovered how 'twas done. When you started playin' to the very beginnin' you was suppaused to write down yer name 'pon the card an' the number o' the table where you started to. Wull, Judy started to table number twenty-nine, which was highest o' the lot. But instaid o' puttin' 29 in the proper place her wraut it up over the cullum where you putts down how many tricks you make. So when her come to cast up the whole lot her included this-yer 29. An' bein', I spause, a bit exzited, the jidges did the same likewise.

An' when they told her nex' day that her ought to return the prize her said the same as her did by the ace : " Wance you let'n go you can't never git 'en back again."

I mus' say I was glad when the ole wiss drive was ovver, an' us come to the dancin' part, cuz I reckoned I wude be abble to injoy a jig around with mother.

But laur' bless 'ee 'twas wiss than tother caper . What alterations from what it use to be ! Wance 'pon a time us use to have a waltz, an' a polka, an' a shotteze, an' lancers, an' quadrills, an' a vew more like o' that. An' I was abble to keep up-sides with the best o'm ; cuz us use to dance 'em all proper, same as they was intended to be danced, an' keep time with the music. A rare hand fer dance-music ole George Cann was, an' use to knack out the time with his voot on the floor all the time he was playin' !

But laur bless yer 'art. the tunes they played up to thik ole dance had'n got rime ner raison in 'em. An' as fer the dances, well there, I don't call 'tis dancin' 't all. I don't zee no dancin' in it. They ban't standin' still, 'tis true, but that's the utmost you can zay fer't. Better-fit they was, most o'm, fer all the dancin' they do's.

There wad'n a polka, ner a shotteze, ner a set o' quadrills all the night. There was a waltz or two I'll admit, but, 'pon me zaul I shude'n a-knawed they was waltzes if it had'n a-bin named on the list o' rules. 'Twad'n no more like a proper waltz than my ole hoss is like the King o' Jericho. When us use to waltz us use to turn round an' round in time to the music, an' go all around the rume suant an' viddy, an' not go bumpin' wan 'gin tother. In fac', I use orwiz to count to mezell wan-two-dree, wan-two-dree, to keep proper time.

But from what I can zee o' the waltzing now-a-days it daun' make a bit of odds whe'er you counts wan-two-dree or vive-leb'm-eight. 'Tis nort else but strakin' about the rume, that's what I caals it. I thought p'raps if I watched 'em gwain fer a bit, an' took notice, I shude sainse it bim-bye. But, laur massey, the longer I watched 'em the more addle-'aided I got. There wad'n no more idea in the way they was walkin' about than if they'd bin zo many caalves in a coort. I daun' believe they knawed theirzells where they was gwain. Fust they'd go vore a bit, then they'd go back, an' then they'd rin thurt-ways an' get in the way of some other couple. Then they stap completely an' think what ole gammut they cude under-take next.

But as fer they new-fangled dances they beats me completely. When 'twas a waltz me an' mother cude do a bit to it in our ole-vashin way, 'till zome scammle-vooted toad come scat up agin us an' knacked me off me countin'. Then us had to start ovver again.

But all they ole vox-trots an' turkey-trots, an' wan-staps an' two-staps, an' all the rest o'm I'm popped if I cude make tap or tail o' they. I've zeed a vew voxes wan time an' another, an' I've rared plenty o' turkeys, but I've never zeed none carry on sitch antics as they was.

Fust they'd walk a bit, an' then they'd rin a bit, an' then they'd stap an' blaw a bit. Then they'd hop a bit an' kicky a bit, an' then they wobble vore an' back. Then they'd vall out, an' make wise to push wan tother out droo the winder, an' then they'd make it up an' pull 'en back again. Then he'd putt out his voot an' her wude jump ovver it, an' arter that he'd shove her along in front fer a bit, an' come dappin along behind. Then her'd putt out her voot an' he wude try to stap on it, so's she'd have to flip'n away quick. Then they'd putt wan voot down an' look at 'en, an' they'd think he did'n look viddy there so they'd pick'n up an' putt'n down someplace else, an' take another look at'n. An' arter all they'd pick'n up an' putt'n back where he was to fust. Then the fella wude try to bend the maiden in ha'f, back'ards, an' jis' as her was gwain to break off like a carrot he'd putt her back straight again. Then, all to wance, they'd make up their mind to dance, an' away-da-go like mad fer a

couple o' staps an' finish with the same, an'
back to their ole no-sainse tattics again.
An' all the time her'd be hangin' on to he
as if he was savin' her from a house avire.
I never did zee sitch attitudes as they
maidens had fer hangin' on to the men.
Seemin' to me they'd ketch 'em hole by
the hair o' the haid, or the yers, or by the
nawse if necessary.

Wull there, I spause 'tis as Tom Zalter
saith, they can't be too pa'ticler now-a-days
with the scarceness of men about. They
mus' ketch 'em best way they can while
they'm gwain. Thing is, whe'er they'm
worth havin' arter they'm ketched.

In the Higher Sphere.

A DEVONSHIRE DRAMA*.

DRAMATIS PERSONÆ :—

REUBEN LEY—a retired farmer and dealer, who has acquired much wealth, but no polish.

MRS. LEY—his wife, who materially assisted in acquiring the wealth, and has also acquired polish in spots.

MARION LEY—their daughter—late Mary Ann—who has " been polished " at a ladies' school.

SIR CHARLES CARTON—highly polished.

EDWARD CARTON—his son, who gets polished off.

Scene :

The Morning Room at Coombe Manor (the new estate of the Leys).

Mrs. Ley and Marion discovered, the former busily attending to details of arrangement about the room.

Marion : Now, mother, I'm sure you have seen to everything. Do sit down and rest a little while you have the chance. You will be completely exhausted presently when the guests arrive.

Mrs. Ley : My dear, I'm so frightened that something will be forgot. If there's a hitch anywhere this afternoon I should never forgive myself. There will be one or two only too ready to laugh if everything doesn't go suant.

Marion : But there isn't going to be any hitch, mother; and I thought you were not going to say " suant " any more.

Mrs. Ley : There, my dear, that's one of the words I was going to leave off. But the nearer we get to the garden party the more flurried I feel, and I'm so feared of making a scummer of it.

Marion : Not " scummer," dear.

Mrs. Ley : Ah! there I go again, cheel.

Marion : " Child," mother.

Mrs. Ley : Aw, dear me. I be gettin' right back as bad as ever again, and forgetting all you've learned me—teached me—taught me I should say.

Marion : You're getting too agitated, mumsie. Keep cool, there's a dear. After all, what does it matter if you do favour our guests with a little Anglo-Saxon?

Mrs. Ley : Oh! my dear. I should die of shame. It's not for myself I mind, but for your sake I must keep up-sides with the rest.

Marion : (Kissing her) Mother, how dare you! As if I would ever wish for any change in the dear parents who love me so, and have done so much for me.

Mrs. Ley : My darling! I know. But us must study this world a little bit—I mean we must. Yes, dear, I'm too excited altogether. I must try to calm myself down a bit. But I'm so anxious for this garden party to be a success. So much depends upon it, and it will give us such a standing in the neighbourhood. Especially now that Sir Charles has promised to come so far, and in his motor-car and all. Think what Mrs. Henderson will feel like to see a fine great motor pull up at our fore-gate—er, front gate—with a coat-of-arms on the door and a whats-its-name in livery on the box.

Marion : Chauffeur, ma.

Mrs. Ley : Yes. What is it again? Show-fer (meditatively), show-fer, show-fer. Yes, I won't forget that (dramatically) John, tell Sir Charles's sofer—show-fer—to take the car around to the coach-'ouse, and see he has something to eat.

Marion : The car, or the chauffeur?

Mrs. Ley : Oh, did I say that wrong, my love?

Marion : No, mother. You said it beautifully It was only my nonsense.

Mrs. Ley : Sit down for a minute, my pet, do'ee, and let me try to recover a little composition. You know, my dear, it's your father that worries me. He doesn't seem to be able to rise to the new spear.

Marion : Sphere.

Mrs. Ley : Ah! yes (with difficulty) S-p-phere. I think I must leave that word alone just yet, dear. I can never say it without spitting. But your father, you see, dear, he's been farmering all these years, and although we've made such a heap of money, now that we've retired and set up like any other gentlefolks, he can't seem to get his mind out of the old rut. The Ley side never wasn't quite the family the Parkinses was.

Marion : You mean the Ley side never was, dear.

Mrs. Ley : No, my love, they never wasn't. You corrected me too soon that time. The Leys never wasn't so high-minded as the Parkinses, and you takes after your mother's side. And since us have—I mean, since we have gived 'ee—given 'ee—given you I should say—such a splendid education at the highest class boardin' school, you'm the equal of any lady in the land.

Marion : Oh! nonsense, dear. I shall be fortunate if I make as good a woman as my mother, or keep as noble a heart as my dear father.

83

Mrs. Ley :	But, unfortunately, your poor father doesn't seem to be able to raise his mind above the turmots—turnips—and the price of winter oats. My dear! Only to see the works I've had this blessed day to keep him from wearing breeches and leggin's at the garden party this afternoon! Whatever would Sir Charles and Mr. Edward have thought ?
Marion :	Really, dear. I don't think that either Sir Charles Carton or Mr. Edward would have minded in the least. From what I saw of them during my stay at Carton Park in the holidays I should say there is nothing of the snob about either of them.
Mrs. Ley :	But, my dear, breeches at a garden party !
Marion :	Dreadful. As bad as wearing bathing costume at a wedding.
Mrs. Ley :	Marion, my dear ! But you know how much people of that class, I mean our class, think of breed. And your father wants such a lot of instruction. He gives himself away every time he opens his mouth. I'm always feared what he's going to say nex'.
Marion :	I think we had better leave dad alone, dear. We shall only muddle him if we try to improve him any more. And, besides, he'll do all right, you see.
Mrs. Ley :	Well, dear, I only hope he will ; but he do make use of such grammar. Yer he comes——
	(Enter Reuben Ley L).
Reuben :	Well, Mary, my dear (takes Marion in his arms).
Mrs. Ley :	Reuben, why don't you call the child Marion ?
Reuben :	Laur ! my swit'art, what do it matter what you'm called so long's you ban't called too late fer dinner. But I'll call

	'ee anything you like to plaize 'ee, though I mus' say I likes Mary best, arter that. Your mother was called it and so was mine. But that's no odds. Why, to plaize 'ee I've dressed meself up like a monkey on a stick.
Mrs. Ley :	Nonsense. You look like a gentleman now.
Reuben :	'Ees. 'Bout as much like a gen'lman as the craw looked like a paycock. Wull, now, what is it I got to do again ?
Marion :	Now listen, daddy, and I'll show you once more. You've simply got to stand at the top of the steps in the middle walk beside mother (Reuben imitates the various actions in a stiff manner) and receive the guests. You bow gracefully to each one, so, and shake hands, so (gives him a " society " shake), not up and down like that, like a pump handle, and then you say, Ah ! how do you do ? So glad you've been able to come. Beautiful weather we're having, isn't it ? Do try and enjoy yourself. I hope so-and-so is well.
Reuben :	Aw ! And you expect me to go through all they monkey tricks ? Why, I couldn't do it in a lifetime.
Marion :	Oh, it's nothing to do, dad. It's quite easy. You try with me. (Marion retires and advances as visitor).
Reuben :	What is it again ? Ah ! yer you be, I see. How be 'ee, then ?
Marion :	Oh ! dad, that's dreadful. Can't you say How do you do ?
Reuben :	Aw, yes. How d'ye do, isn't it ? Well, get back there again, and let's have another try. (Marion advances). Ullaw, how d'ee do, then ? Plaized to zee 'ee. Make yerself at 'ome. I wish you was there.
Marion :	No, no, dad. Not that.

Reuben :   No, no. That wouldn't be viddy,
            would it ? No, try again. Ah ! how
            d'ee du ? 'Ope you'll injoy yerself.
            You'll find plenty to ait an' plenty to
            drink.

Marion :   I didn't say that, dad.

Reuben :   That's all right, my dear. I never
            knowed any man affronted by having
            his stomach provided for. An' what
            else is it I've got to say ? How's
            missis, or how's maister, 'cording to
            which isn't there. Now have I got it
            right, my dear ?

Marion :   Why, yes, daddy—it—it isn't bad—
            only (commences to cry) (Reuben folds
            her in his arms).

Reuben :   I see, my dear. You think your old
            daddy can't come to it. Well, you
            ban't far wrong, my precious. No—no
            —I can see as far through a brick wall
            as most men, and I can see you'm
            wonderin' what Sir Charles Carton or
            what Mr. Edward Carton will think to
            see the lovely Miss Marion's father
            behavin' in such a uncivilised manner.
            Now, my lovely. I ban't scoldin' of
            'ee, but I can suggest a good way out
            o't. Let your mother do all the bowin'
            an' the scrapin', an' the how-d'ee-doing
            outside, and I'll bide in 'ere : an' if any
            of the men-folk like to come in an' sit
            down, an' smok' an' tell a bit, why, I'll
            be here for 'em to laugh at if they've a
            mind to.

Marion :   (Indignantly). No one had better let
            me see him laughing at my father.

Reuben :   That's all right, my dear. Daddy can
            look arter hisself. Now I can 'eer a
            motor comin'. You'd better-way be
            off and see to the receptionising.

Mrs. Ley : (Agitatedly) Oh ! Marion. Wait a bit.
            Can it be Sir Charles, I wonder. Marion,
            am I looking red ? Dear me, I'm all to

	a commotion. Marion, did you say I should sound the haitch in honner or no ? Which is it ?
Marion :	Honour, dear. Not honner.
Mrs. Ley :	(Rehearsing). Dear Sir Charles, this is a honner—a honour——
Marion :	An, dear, not a.
Mrs. Ley :	Yes, of course, this is an honner—no, no, a nonner,—a nonner.
	(Exeunt Mrs. Ley and Marion R).
Reuben :	(Laughing). Aw, dear, dear, dear ! What fules us do make oursel's sooner than appear natteral. Ah, well ! gimme a day's ploughin' or harvestin' before all this tomfoolishness. I wonder what sort o' chap this yer Zir Charles is ? A fella with a handle to his name like that sure to be stuck up, and full o' pride, and regard the like o' me as the dirt under his foot. Well, I ban't gwain to have it. I've always lived honest, and traited me neighbour same's I should wish for 'en to trait me, an' nobody can't say more'n that, even if he's a sir, or a duke, or a king for the matter o' that. But a man can't alter his nature, and 'tis useless to put a pig in a loose-box and expect 'en to come out a race-'oss. But I'd better-way go an' waish me hands and brish up me hair a bit. Must make the best o' what there is, I spaus.
	(Exit L.) (Enter Mrs. Ley, Marion, Sir Charles, and Edward R).
Mrs. Ley :	Come in, Sir Charles. I'm sure you'd like to sit and rest a bit after such a long journey. Mr. Ley will be proud to meet you, and you men folk can sit and Why, where's he to ? Dear me. I smoke, and tel—talk, I mean. Reubin ! thought my husband was in yer—in here. But he won't be a minute, Sir Charles. You'll excuse me running away, but I must look after the other

87

	guestis—guess'. Marion, my love, you can entertain Sir Charles and Mr. Edward 'till your father comes.
Edward :	I'm not a scrap tired, Mrs. Ley, really.
Sir C. :	No, no. You young people go out and enjoy yourselves. I'll be glad of the rest and quiet till Mr. Ley returns. Don't trouble, Mrs. Ley, I'll introduce myself. I'm sure neither of us will mind waiving such a minor detail of etiquette.
Mrs. Ley :	Really, Sir Charles, it's so very kind of you to be so—so—condensating.
Sir C. :	Not at all, my dear madam. Kind of you to permit me to make myself at home. Edward, my boy, no need to have armed ourselves against the elements, after all. Leave me your mac. and umbrella.
Mrs. Ley :	(Making to ring). The maid shall take them.
Sir C. :	No, no. The servants are all as busy as they can be ; don't bother. I'll carry them out in a minute with my own. (Hangs both coats over his arm and takes both umbrellas in his hand). Now clear out you two and play tennis while I rest half an hour, then I'll come and beat both of you with one hand behind my back. (Exeunt Mrs. Ley, Marion, and Edward R). By Jove ! that poor woman's efforts to be un-natural will take ten years off her life. (Enter Reuben L).
Reuben :	(Aside) Ullaw ! Zir Charles's footman, I suppose. (Sir Charles places coats on the back of a chair). That's right, my good fella. Stick 'em down any place. I'll carr' 'em out bim'by.
Sir C. :	Ah ! How do you do ? Mr. Ley, is it not ?
Reuben :	That's right, my boy. I thought your master was in yer, but I'm glad he isn't,

	to tell 'ee the truth. Sit down a minute. I ban't in any tremenjus hurry to meet 'en.
Sir C. :	(Aside). Evidently he takes me for a servant. Thank you. Will you have a cigar ?
Reuben :	Thank'ee. Wan o' Sir Charles's, I reckon ? (Sir C. nods). I thought so. You footmen be all alike. I wouldn't trust nuther-one of 'ee so far as I could sling a cow by the tail.
Sir C. :	You have never met Sir Charles, then ?
Reuben :	No, not 'eet. Must, I 'spose. But 'tis a ordeal I'd sooner be spared from. My darter have met 'en through the means o' gwain to the same school as Zir Charles's maid, an' gwain down to Carton Park to spend a holiday. Us'll be foced to ax 'em back again. I 'spose, but I dreads it.
Sir C. :	You do ?
Reuben :	'Ees. Properly dreads it, I do. You see, Mr.—er—I didn't quite ketch your name——
Sir C. :	Oh—er—they don't call me by my name, you see—simply Charles.
Reuben :	I zee. Charles the footman. All right, I'll call 'ee Charles, an' I should be very glad for you to call me Reuben.
Sir C. :	I'm afraid my master would scarcely be pleased to hear me——
Reuben :	Your master, be blowed ! What's it got to do with he, what I mind for you to call me ? Look yer, Charles, I tell'ee what 'tis. I hardly ever hears my own name now-a-days. There was a time, back in the old village, when I was Reuben Lay to every man, wumman, an' cheel in the parish. Now, begad, I'm Mister Lee, Esquire, and us be got up into what my wife calls a higher spear.

89

Sir C.:	You prefer plain Reuben, then ?
Reuben:	Yes, I du. A plain name for a plain man. I often wish to gudeness that I'd never made all this money. I don't like this yer higher spear. I ban't suited to it, and nobody can't make me suited to it, so it's redecklus for'm to try. Might as well try to taiche a dog to eat hay. My old friends in the farmerin' days was honest, and spaked out their minds. But now-a-days, caw bless my saul, I never knaws what they'm cringing and crawling around me for. They flatters me to me face, and they laughs at me behind me back, and then they comes and borreys fifty pound. This master o' yours ten to one he'll be so polite an' nice, an' bow an' scrape, an' then go back to his friends an' make a laughin' sport of old Reuben Ley as if I was a wild beast show.
Sir C.:	Oh! I don't know. I don't think he will.
Reuben:	Well, us'll zee. Be-as-'twill, I don't owe him naught. So it don't make a hap'my odds to me what he thinks. If he don't like it yer he must lump it, that's all. Now, Charles, me boy, what will 'ee take to drink with me ? There's all the nu-fangled things here, port or sherry—or there's a drap o' gude whisky, or if yu like to say the word I can get 'ee a pint o' cider in two minutes.
Sir C.:	Thanks, I'll have just a little port.
Reuben:	Right you be. Then I'll join 'ee in the same, though I calls these little drinks is making a fool of a man's mouth. Charles, me boy, yer's to 'ee.
Sir C.:	Your health, Reuben. (They drink).
Reuben:	Now, I wonder what they fools be up to out in the garden. Let's go in 'tother houze, us can zee 'em out o' winder. (Exeunt L. Enter Marion and Edward R).

Marion :	Come in, Mr. Carton, will you? Sir Charles——Oh! I am so sorry. I thought my father and Sir Charles would have been here. Let us go and find them.
Edward :	(Leading Marion to a chair) Not unless you would very much rather, Miss Ley. Let us wait here until they return. I know you are heated and tired. Sit down and rest a while.
Marion :	I must not be long away from mamma. She is so busy.
Edward :	Not for long. Only for a few short minutes. And yet those minutes mean a whole lifetime to me—a lifetime of joy and happiness, or an existence over-shadowed by an eternal regret. Miss Ley, I am a man of few words, and not gifted with eloquence. However much I might strive to coin gilded phrases my heart-beats forge them all into the one measure which throbs through my blood at every pulse, and sings along my brain till the whole world seems reverberant with the strain I love you! I love you! Marion, that is what I came to tell you to-day. I have told it bluntly and uncouthly, but truly, and because my heart could contain it no longer . . . Marion, what have you to say to me?
Marion :	What can I say, Mr. Carton? No woman could hear from a true man what I have heard from you without feeling proud. And I am very proud, indeed, but——
Edward :	Then make me proud, too. Make me the proudest man on earth, and tell me that you love me . . . . or that you—you might learn to love me. . . Marion, or even that you do not hate me . . . . Tell me something.
Marion :	I do not hate you, Mr. Carton. I like you very much indeed; but——

91

Edward :	But what, my loved one ?
Marion :	(Rising and moving away) We ought not to be speaking of this at all.
Edward :	Why ought we not ?
Marion :	Because, don't you see, it is selfish in you.
Edward :	I know it is selfish in me to ask for the whole love of one so beautiful and good, but I do ask it, and——
Marion :	You misunderstand me, Mr. Carton. You are forgetting your—your family.
Edward :	(Crossing and leading her to a seat) I think I understand you now, Miss Ley. Sit down there, and I'll sit here, where we can see one another face to face. That is, I'll stay here if I can. Now, I said once before that I have not the gift of many words. Pray forgive me if my earnestness appears to carry me beyond the borders of politeness, for the whole of my future life, in so far as it is to be worth living, is in your gift. Now, miss, sentiment on one side. I am going to examine you in your catechism. You will kindly answer me without hesitation or equivocation. (Marion leans forward interlacing her fingers and resting her hands on her knees). I er—don't think you had better come quite so near as that, or the examiner may find some difficulty in . . . (Marion sits bolt upright). Now, miss, tell me, do you mean your late remarks to bear reference to the er—relative social standing of your family and mine ?
Marion :	I do.
Edward :	Do you intend to imply that if I married you—no, no, look straight at me, miss— in that case my godfathers and god-mothers and things, and the rest of my relations, might be annoyed ?
Marion :	I do.

92

Edward : Do you consider that in this matter I am called upon to consider my relations one little bit ?

Marion : I do.

Edward : Well, I don't. However ! Do you consider that if my father gave his consent to my choice (I having, as you know, no mother), I might ignore the rest of my relations ?

Marion : I do.

Edward : Do you forgive me for declaring my love for you as I have done ?

Marion : I do (giving Edward her hand, which he kisses).

Edward : Do you feel glad that I have so done ?

Marion : (With some embarrassment) I do.

Edward : (Fervently). Marion, do you love me ? (Marion's head sinks into her hands. Edward, on his knee at her side, draws her hands away, and retains his hold of them. Marion recovers herself and looks at Edward).

Marion : I do.

Edward : Darling ! And if our parents agree do you consent to become my wife ?

Marion : I do. (Rises).

Edward : One more question, my darling, only one more. In the circumstances do you, or do you not, think that I might venture to kiss you ?

Marion : (Smiling) I do.
(Edward does). (Enter Mrs. Ley R).

Mrs. Ley : Oh ! I beg your pardon.

Edward : Not at all, Mrs. Ley. Your having caught us makes my explanation easy as far as your are concerned. Let me say, then, in short, that Marion has promised to be my wife subject to the approval of our respective parents. (Proffering his hand). Mrs. Ley, say you approve of me as a son.

(Mrs. Ley takes Edward's hand in both her own, but does not trust herself to speak. Edward bends his head and kisses her hand. He raises his head and Mrs. Ley kisses his forehead. She then folds Marion in her arms. Edward moves R).

(Voices heard off L).

Marion : (Moving L). Here come the pa's.

Edward : Now to be a Daniel !

(Enter Reuben and Sir Charles L. in conversation).

Reuben : Ah ! here's a few of 'em, I zee. Now, Charles, you'd better way be bustling around, and see what's to be done.

Marion : (Aside to Edward) Charles !

Edward : (Aside to Marion). They're on jolly good terms, at any rate.

Mrs. Ley : Oh ! Sir Charles. I'm afraid you've had a very dull time.

Reuben : (Sinking into chair). Sir Charles ! Is that Sir Charles ?

Sir C. : Indeed no, Mrs. Ley. On the contrary—

Mrs. Ley : Why, Reuben, what are you talking about ?

Reuben : Aw, my blessid. An' I've just let him brish my coat !

Sir C. : And why should I not brush your coat, Reuben Ley ? Honest men are not so plentiful that we can afford to miss the opportunity of brushing the coat of one when we find him.

Reuben : (Rising quickly). Sir Charles Carton, you an't traited me fair an' square.

Sir C. : Don't say that, my friend. You deceived yourself, and perhaps I was wrong in permitting the self-deception to continue. But, at any rate, I am the gainer of a friend whom I am proud to own as such. That is, Reuben, if you think my friendship worth having. (Offers his hand).

94

Reuben : (After a pause, during which he gazes motionless at Sir Charles—gripping his hand). Charles, thee art a man. More'n that I couldn't say to the King hisself.

Edward : (Advancing). Excuse me, sirs, there is one other matter awaiting your judgment. I have asked Marion to marry me, and her decision rests entirely upon your consent . . . Gentlemen . . . two lives are in your hands. (Sir Charles and Reuben look at one another in silence. Then Marion approaches her father and creeps into his arms. Sir Charles takes Edward's hand).

Sir C. : Reuben . . . my son, to be your son.

Reuben : (Giving Marion's hand to Edward) Charles, my daughter, to be your daughter.

Sir C. : And may God bless them both. (Edward and Marion move R. Reuben takes the hands of his wife, L. Sir Charles centre).

Reuben : Amen. And thanks be for such a happy result to ole Reuben Ley's fus' day in the Higher Spear.

THE WESTERN MORNING NEWS CO., LTD.,

PRINTERS, PLYMOUTH